W9-DJN-663

Matta   "Le Vertige d'Eros" 1944 · Ektachrome courtesy the Museum of Modern Art, New York City

The Art of Organic Forms

PHILIP C. RITTERBUSH

SMITHSONIAN INSTITUTION PRESS

City of Washington

Smithsonian Publication 4740
Library of Congress catalog card number 68-31365

Designed by Stephen Kraft

Preface

I have long desired to present an exhibit that would express the creative, imaginative character of science by demonstrating its affinities with the arts. This book is an attempt to justify and account for such an exhibit, held in the Museum of Natural History in Washington from June 14 to July 31, 1968. It owes its origin to the calmly revolutionary suggestion of André Schiffrin, a valued adviser of the Smithsonian, that we at the Institution come to regard exhibits as the iconography for books that should be written. Partly because exhibits can be attempts at direct persuasion on controversial subjects I accepted this as a welcome opportunity to prepare a book-length study in a way that would take advantage of the existence of the exhibit. This book is the report of a rather hasty exploratory reconnaissance, a brief adventure of ideas. It is an historical sketch of a fruitful and protean concept, which I have called the idea of organic form, the notion that organized beings display principles of emergent order of greater complexity than nonliving entities, whereby organic form is seen to be a property of the whole organism, in distinction to the forms of its parts or subordinate elements.

The main body of the exhibit consists of works of art—painting, graphics, and sculpture—and a few texts that may help the viewer to grasp the character of the forms presented, which suggest the visual content of the science of biology and more particularly resemble those of cells and protozoa that lie beyond the range of unaided vision. What do organic motifs in abstract art have to tell us about science and imagination? If that seems a legitimate question to ask, linger amidst an expressive profusion of forms in this unusual collection of works of art and experience them directly. The plates at the back of the book and the catalogue of the exhibit with such suggestive titles as *Cellular Construction, Proteus Changing, Lemur,* and *Prenez garde au microbe de l'amour* can be no substitute for experiencing the works themselves.

In ancillary exhibit halls there are displays along two themes, which each visitor is asked to acknowledge. The first is that the progress of biology depends upon the biologist's faculty for the invention of form in accord with certain presuppositions about what will prove to be of scientific value. The second is that beauty in nature is more than skin deep, that symmetry principles and rhythmic harmonies find objective existence in organisms. These are two corollaries of the idea of organic form and if the viewer has understood them he is well prepared to view the exhibit. These propositions are set forth at greater length in chapters three and four of this book, the general purpose of which is to establish their esthetic and scientific relevance. If you believe, however, that science is no more than the accumulation of facts, a social process susceptible of computerization, whose future will unfold unerringly without imaginativeness and a capacity to dream, an ant-hill kind of enterprise that can be bureaucratized, then turn away. The viewer of this exhibit should also be willing to seek beauty in unexpected, unconventional places such as under a microscope, in an aquarium, or in a museum of natural history.

It has been my privilege for four years to serve as a staff assistant to S. Dillon Ripley, eighth Secretary of the Smithsonian Institution, who believes that the museum should be the home of conjecture and the resort of the imagination. Unless these qualities are given wide scope, knowledge will accumulate in museums like fossilizing sediments on the sea floor, a stygian process of concern to only a few misshapen bottom-dwellers sifting through it for their private amusement. Rather it is the role of the museum to exploit the wide social relevance of knowledge, above all its beauty and boundless fascination, and to safeguard it for our future. For the support Mr. Ripley has provided to this undertaking and the leave of absence granted to give me an opportunity to explore the subjects discussed in this book I am most grateful. I hope this exhibit conforms to his challenging concept of the museum.

Mounting an exhibit is a complex enterprise that everyone should experience at least once, in order to appreciate the effort that lies behind the simplest case containing objects. To the lenders of works of art listed in the catalogue I am deeply grateful. I also thank the staff of the Smithsonian Institution: the Office of Exhibits under the direction of John Anglim; the U.S. National Museum under the direction of Frank A. Taylor; the staff of the Museum of Natural

History and its able director Richard S. Cowan; the Libraries, especially Jack Marquardt for his unfailing helpfulness; the Joseph H. Hirshhorn Museum and Sculpture Garden whose Director, Abram Lerner, offered frequent advice; the Photographic Services Division and the Smithsonian Institution Press. All have been unstinting in their help, and if I may single out a few by name I wish to record my particular gratitude to Abigail Booth, Lloyd Hermann, Lee Hogenson, Harry Lowe, Charles Lundquist, Robert Mason, Walter Shropshire, and Kenneth Towe for helping in especially important ways. Diana Hamilton, without whose command of its most subtle aspects the exhibit would have been impossible, has served with distinction as research assistant responsible for implementing the exhibit program through selection of the works of art and managing the delicate process of borrowing and returning them. She is author of the catalogue of the exhibit. Cecelia Howe gave most welcome clerical assistance in preparing the manuscript, and I am delighted to acknowledge the artistic skill with which Michael Clark addressed himself to preparing the line drawings in the text. Those marked as "after" a given work, in distinction to photographs "from" it, are by his hand.

The designer of the exhibit, whose advice contributed greatly to its effectiveness, was Lucius E. Lomax.

To my colleagues who so kindly discussed this book in the course of its preparation I am deeply grateful. I hope they will regard it as the report of a brief voyage of discovery and offer suggestions for further exploration.

Philip C. Ritterbush
Washington, D. C.
February 1968

To *G. Evelyn Hutchinson*

Sterling Professor of Zoology
Yale University

this book is dedicated

On the same terms, therefore, as art is attained to, is all knowledge and science acquired; for as art is a habit with reference to things to be done, so is science a habit in respect to things to be known: as that proceeds from the imitation of types or forms, so this proceeds from the knowledge of natural things. Each has its origin in sense and experience, and it is impossible that there can rightly be either art or science without visible instance or example.

William Harvey

Contents

Preface   i

I.   To Set Form above Nature   1

II.   Esthetics and Analogies to Life   16

III.   A Tissue of Imagining   26

IV.   Living Symmetry   42

V.   The Progress of Biological Forms   73

VI.   A Catalogue of the Exhibit   95

Plates   109

References   133

Index   141

To Set Form I above Nature

JOHANN WOLFGANG von Goethe (1749-1832), the towering eminence of German letters, was a highly prolific writer whose active career spanned six decades. *Faust,* his greatest work, was published in 1808 and has stood ever since as the central landmark of German literature. It must be confessed that the enormity of his experience of nature and art, the vastness of his influence upon the Romantic Movement, make Goethe a somewhat intimidating object for those who seek to understand his thought, a genius so many-sided as to be almost unapproachable. Yet there is a single quality of this most remarkable man that unfailingly makes him accessible to us—his sense of beauty in nature. From earliest childhood he experienced a vivid and intensely sympathetic sense of wonder at nature. In an anecdote of early boyhood in his autobiography *Dichtung und Wahrheit* he tells how he built a pyramid of natural history specimens on his father's music stand, on top of which he kindled incense with a burning glass from the rays of the rising sun, "signifying the aspirations of man's heart towards his Maker." He became a lifelong student of geology, botany, comparative anatomy, physiological optics, and many aspects of natural philosophy. In all of these fields he wrote extensively, gave frequent lectures, and entered into correspondence with leading savants. In a number of these contributions he was led astray by his sense of beauty in a manner that destroyed their value from a strict scientific standpoint.

Yet they represent a remarkable synthesis of scientific aspirations and esthetic appreciation, which may serve as a starting place for our inquiry into the historical background of the twentieth-century art of organic forms.

To an historian concerned with the progressive establishment of correct scientific knowledge, Goethe would appear to have been uncritical in speculating about nature. He was little interested in experiments and preferred to draw his ideas from contemplation and intuition (*Anschauung*). He aspired to knowledge through direct insight, seeking a mental representation of the qualities of nature rather than an explanation of factors whose operation could be measured. In my earlier study of scientific explanation in biology during the eighteenth century and the Romantic period, I portrayed the years around the turn of the century as a time when chemists and biologists had begun to apply in their work the lessons of method to be drawn from the physical sciences.[1] Biologists had gained an awareness that the phenomena of life were not to be explained all at once as a result of an intuitive leap or philosophical precept, but through a painstakingly slow and deliberate analysis of the structure and characteristics of organisms. As one careful scientific worker of the time put it, the factors affecting the process of nutrition were all interrelated like strands in a complex knot, which was not to be cut through all at once but must instead be patiently untied. Investigators whose contributions have persisted from that time as secure elements in the structure of scientific knowledge, chemists such as Antoine Lavoisier, Jöns Jakob Berzelius, and Sir Humphry Davy, or physiologists such as Jean Senebier, Nicolas Théodore de Saussure, and Jan Ingenhousz, cautioned against speculation and insisted upon a critical approach—modest, but more certain in the treatment of natural phenomena. Goethe was well aware of this tendency toward empiricism among the scientific writers of his time, but his pregnant intuitions were not to be stifled by their caution.

To a thoughtful observer in the decades around 1800 the results of experiment would have fallen far short of accounting for the apparent qualities of organisms —their vital energies and the processes of growth and reproduction. There had been a few careful and systematic observers, men like Stephen Hales, Antoine de Réaumur, Abraham Trembley, and John Hunter, but life processes remained mysterious and unexplained. The discovery that plants emit oxygen in sunlight was not made until 1774, by Joseph Priestley, who lacked the understanding of oxidation as a chemical process that he needed for a proper interpretation of this fact. In 1791 Luigi Galvani claimed to have proved that static electricity provided the motive force of animals, but soon thereafter his statements were refuted by Volta and others, who demonstrated that the electrical phenomena manifested by organisms must arise from chemical reactions whose relation to electricity was only beginning to be understood. The principal facts relating to

[1] *Overtures to Biology* (1964).

the fertilization of flowering plants were described by Joseph Koelreuter in the 1760s, but he ascribed the effects of pollen to streams of invisible and highly attenuated subtle gas which eluded further investigation. The limited character of such results as these and the difficulties of interpreting them could do little to satisfy the strong appetite for understanding felt by a man of Goethe's outlook. Science progresses in large measure as a result of ignoring what there seems no possibility of explaining. The resulting limits upon explanation have given rise to discomfort even to scientists, while to many thinkers of the Romantic period such limits were intellectually affronting—a challenge to their imaginations to devise comprehensive systems of explanation sufficient to account for all the phenomena of life.

Goethe had frequently noticed that individuals of a given species of plant were to be found growing to different sizes or in varying forms, depending on whether they occurred in mountains or lowlands, in light or in shade. He was one of the first students of environmental influences on plants, an aspect of nature that occupies a central position among topics for modern biological research. Yet in his time there was barely any competent understanding of the influence of such factors as light, heat, day length, or gravity upon plant growth, and too little knowledge about the material processes of growth to serve as a basis for sound conjecture about the meaning of his observations. This did not prove to be a serious obstacle to his genius and he set out to formulate a theory of plant life that would do justice to his powers of intuition and express his apprehensions about the central phenomena of growth and form.

Acutely aware of the diversity of shape and structure in plants and longing for some principle by which his observations of the previous ten years could be rationalized, Goethe left Weimar in 1786 for a two-year tour of Italy. As he wrote to Frau von Stein before leaving, the plant kingdom was raging in his mind. He felt that he stood on the brink of a great discovery. "And it is no dream, no fantasy, it is the awareness of the essential form with which Nature is, as it were, always toying and in the course of play brings forth the infinite variety of life." [2] At the botanical garden in Padua he was overwhelmed by the beauty and variety of the plants he beheld. If only he could discover for all plants a single source to which any form might be traced. He did not mean an ultimate ancestor of plants in an evolutionary sense, but rather gave it as his belief that there was an ideal type from which all other plants could be derived intellectually. The *Urpflanze,* as he styled it, would express the essence of vegetative life directly to its beholder. It would typify all of the different kinds of plant life. He expected to know it at once if he came upon it. In April of 1787 in the Public Gardens at Palermo, while musing upon the plot of a play to be based on the Odyssey, he had these thoughts:

[2] H. E. Gerlach and O. Herrmann, *Goethe erzählt sein Leben* (Frankfurt: Fischer Bücherei, 1956), pp. 218-219.

Seeing so much new and burgeoning growth, I came back to my old notion and wondered whether I might not chance upon my archetypal plant. There must be such a plant, after all. If all plants were not molded on one pattern, how could I recognize that they *are* plants? . . . My fine poetic resolutions were frustrated. The garden of Alcinous had vanished. In its place the garden of the world opened up. Why are we moderns so distraught? Why are we challenged to demands we can neither attain nor fulfill? [3]

A month later he wrote from Rome to his long-standing friend, the poet and writer on human nature, J. G. Herder, that the archetypal plant "will be the strangest growth the world has ever seen." "Nature herself will envy me for it." From such an image an infinite range of plant types could be projected. "They will be imbued with inner truth and necessity. And the same law will be applicable to all that lives."

Goethe did not succeed in finding the primal plant. Rather he altered his idea of it, coming to believe that all plants were composed of modified leaves, except for the stem, which was simply a geometric axis upon which the variations of growth were exhibited. Thus he abstracted from all plants a basic unit, the primordial leaf, which might be expressed as a leaf, a flower part, or a seed capsule. This process of growth through the repetitive elaboration of a basic plan he conceived to depend upon cycles of expansion and contraction whereby organs were formed according to the characteristic rhythm of each plant. After two years' further development of these ideas Goethe incorporated them into his treatise of 1790, "An Attempt by J. W. von Goethe, Privy Councilor of the Duchy of Saxe-Weimer, to Explain the Metamorphosis of Plants." In 1799 he expressed his ideas in the form of a poem which included these lines:

> Oft the beholder marvels at the wealth
> Of shape and structure shown in succulent surface—
> The infinite freedom of the growing leaf.
> Yet nature bids a halt; her mighty hands,
> Gently directing even higher perfection,
> Narrow the vessels, moderate the sap;
> And soon the form exhibits subtle change.

In 1795 Goethe published a paper summarizing rather similar views in the field of the comparative anatomy of vertebrates. Here also he sought an ideal type from which all skeletal forms might be derived. He viewed the animal body as a system of components, no one of which could attain maximum devel-

---

[3] Quoted in Magnus, *Goethe as a Scientist* [1906]. The author was professor of pharmacology at Utrecht and a distinguished investigator of reflex action. His work with Sherrington is related in Ragnar Granit, *Charles Scott Sherrington: An Appraisal* (New York: Doubleday, 1967). The *Italienische Reise*, translated by W. H. Auden and Elizabeth Mayer, was published by Pantheon Books in 1962 in a handsome format, with a number of reproductions of Goethe's sketches and paintings.

opment without proportional reduction in the others. He returned again and again to this interest in comparative anatomy, always in terms of units whose combinations and modifications revealed an ideal plan for organic life.

We must take particular note of the visual character of the idealized plant form. It exists not in nature but in the mind, which it delights with all the vividness of a dream. Goethe sought to understand natural processes by visualizing them. Throughout his works we find a preoccupation with visual experience which was undoubtedly influenced by his youthful ambition to become a painter and his early efforts at painting and drawing. During his Italian journey, for example, he investigated technical aspects of painting, carefully studying the effects produced by the use of different colors and questioning painters about how they worked. He had Angelica Kauffmann paint a variety of landscapes from which the usual colors were omitted, and he compared them with the atmospheric effects he observed in nature. A flower painter might attain accuracy in depicting nature, but that would be mere imitation; Goethe thought that the highest artistic expression required a profound understanding of the flower, its mode of growth, and the effects of the environment, so that its inmost essence could be expressed visually.[4] He published numerous conjectures about the physiological basis of vision which were of some value to Johannes Purkinje (1787-1869) and Johannes Müller (1801-1858), who helped to place physiological optics on a scientific basis a generation later. Above all of his other writings, including his poems and dramas, Goethe valued the *Farbenlehre* (1810), a highly speculative treatise on optics, wherein he argued that the colors of the spectrum are produced by a "primal phenomenon"—the contrast of light and darkness—and that Newton had been mistaken in thinking that white light had been analyzed into components of different colors.

The understanding of nature sought by Goethe was almost exclusively visual: structural elements arranged in a vertebrate column, leaves arranged around an axis, or a chart drawn to show the essentials of plant geography, which he subsequently published. One of his principal recreations was to view aquatic life through the microscope; in 1786 he made detailed drawings of protozoa including paramecium and vorticella. He eagerly corresponded with Eduard Joseph d'Alton (1772-1840) on the subject of scientific illustration. Throughout his life Goethe supposed that he had fathomed the essence of phenomena when he had worked out a means of representing them visually. Such an illustration was most satisfying to him when it could be realized concretely as a chart or diagram, a portrait of organic nature. Thus he had the warmest praise for a chart published in 1821 showing the distribution of life in the world's oceans correlated with climatic factors. He regarded it as a highly successful attempt "to present to the eye, by symbolic means, facts which have

[4] Goethe, "Einfache Nachahmung der Natur, Manier, Stil [1788]," *Goethes Werke,* vol. 27 (Stuttgart: J. G. Cotta, 1868), p. 28.

a sensuous basis yet are not visibly perceptible, so that imagination, memory, and understanding may be stimulated to fill in what is missing." [5]

It is almost impossible to think of modern science without visualizing some of its very elegant and sophisticated constructs of reality: assemblages of spheres representing molecules, graphs and diagrams of all kinds against co-ordinates measuring quantities, or the tree of life showing lines of evolutionary descent. Much explanation in science proceeds through the presentation of vis-ually realized models which represent or at least illustrate the phenomena. In Goethe's day this aspect of the biological sciences was only slightly developed. Naturalists had long thought that the realm of organized nature could be rep-resented by a linear series of organisms arranged ladder-like in a succession of increasingly complex forms: *The Great Chain of Being,* as it was called in the title of a noteworthy historical monograph by Arthur O. Lovejoy in 1936. The great systematic biologist Carl Linnaeus (1707-1778) tried to work out a natural classification of orders and genera of plants based upon this idea, but he found that plant groups displayed more complex affinities and abandoned his attempt in 1750. The distinction between plants and animals, which few eighteenth-century naturalists had found significant, did not attain importance in science until the single ladder scheme was replaced by the notion of a tree whose branches might represent the two kingdoms of organic nature. The earliest use of the tree as a metaphor of this kind which I know in scientific writing is that of the German naturalist Peter Simon Pallas in 1766, but by the early years of the nineteenth century it had become a commonplace for biolo-gists to refer to plants and animals as two branches on a tree of nature. It is worth noting that Charles Darwin did not have to invent a scheme tracing the descent of higher animals from lower; this was a familiar idea, represented first by the linear series and then by the tree of life. Many supposed that Charles Darwin was the first to understand the succession of different forms of life. That is not so. What Darwin discovered and demonstrated, and it was an achievement of epic proportions, was that the origin of species could be formu-lated as a problem in the domain of scientific research, and that the study of variation, inheritance, and selection would confirm the operation of general laws of evolution through natural selection. These references to biological classifi-cation should serve as a reminder that an arrangement of organisms according to their affinities is itself a scheme or model for reality; most naturalists of the eighteenth century worked with abstract representations of nature to at least that extent. But Goethe was well ahead of his contemporaries in perceiving that organisms could be reduced to schematic representations not just on the basis of

---

[5] Goethe, Review of J. B. Wilbrand and F. A. von Ritgen, *Gemälde der organischen Natur in ihrer Verbreitung auf der Erde* (Giessen: C. G. Müller, 1821), in *Goethe's Botanical Writings* (1952), pp. 120-121. They dedicated their book to Goethe, Alexander von Hum-boldt, and J. F. Blumenbach. For more of Goethe's botanical drawings, see J. Schuster, *Goethe, die Metamorphose der Pflanzen mit dem Originalbildwerk* (Berlin: W. Junk, 1924).

comparisons of one with another, but through the relations within their bodies of part to whole.

Biologists refer to the study of form and structure as "morphology," which differs from anatomy in seeking to elucidate the processes governing form rather than to determine the functions of the various components of organisms. Goethe was among the first to use the term; his *Metamorphosis of Plants* was an influential early publication in the field. What distinguishes this work from modern morphological writings is its lack of concern with the material processes by which growth occurs, such as the different structures of the various tissues or the pathways followed by imbibed water. He completely ignores the properties of the substances composing the organism and the processes by which these contribute to its growth. That leaves, petals, and sepals were variations upon a basic element in development had already been proposed by Christian Friedrich Wolff and, less clearly, by Linnaeus. Goethe gives an account of form only in its ideal aspects. The abstraction of the primordial leaf from the varied aspects of the plant explains nothing about the manner in which growth actually occurs, but it is the supreme example of Goethe's desire to project within his own mind a visual impression of the workings of nature. He found it thrilling to apply his abstraction to plants and it satisfied him more than any scientific explanation that his contemporaries could provide (*Figure 1*).

Figure 1. Sketches by Goethe, showing development of stems from nodes and leaves. His script indicates (left) the contraction of stem leaves to the calyx, (center) the succession of nodes, and (right) a node with the leaf. (After *Goethe's Botanical Writings,* 1952, fig. 13, p. 43.)

Compare Goethe's approach to that of Nehemiah Grew (1628-1712), one of the first to study the anatomy of plants, who proposed in 1672 that all plants were composed of four differently shaped crystals of mineral salts; these entered through pores in the roots and combined to form circles or lines which became extended through the addition of ever more such ultramicroscopic crystals in regular patterns.[6] Grew regarded regularities in natural forms as evidence that the processes of growth consisted in the repetition of simple steps, into which forms might successfully be analyzed. The means for doing so were far beyond the science of his day, a century before Goethe, but Grew faithfully believed that microscopic examination of plants might disclose such processes and permit the growth of plants to be explained on mechanical principles. He traced a circle around the outline of leaves as an earnest of his faith that mathematical regularities might be found in all organisms, indicating that regular mechanical processes and nothing more would account for their achieved forms (*Figure* 2).

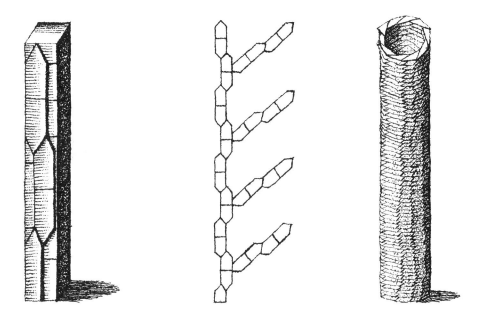

Figure 2. The elements of form. (After Nehemiah Grew, *The Anatomy of Plants* [1682], pl. 53: figs. 7, 9, 16.)

We may style this the analytic approach to form, as opposed to Goethe's idealistic morphology. Grew's notion that growth depended upon the apposition of equal parts was disproved by microscopic investigation of the tissues of organisms, which were found to be exceedingly varied and complex. François Bichat (1771-1802), the brilliant French anatomist, contended that the functions of organisms could best be studied in tissue systems as a whole, ignoring their

[6] Grew, *The Anatomy of Vegetables Begun* [1672].

fine structure, which he judged to be unknowable at least for his time.[7] Bichat took the extreme position of refusing to use a microscope and did not even employ illustrations in his publications. Georges Cuvier (1769-1832), preeminent among the early comparative anatomists, shared Bichat's view that direct examination of organisms was the basis of scientific understanding, but he also conceded the value of an authentic visual representation and drew many himself.[8]

Considered with reference to scientific explanation, Goethe's image of plant development was an illustration rather than a representation. I propose to employ this as a key distinction. All images, artistic or scientific, whether they enter naively or self-consciously into our awareness, are abstractions from diverse phenomena. The abstraction of images occurs even during everyday perception, wherein the mind reduces the richness of sense data to orderly patterns. An image functions as an illustration of an object when it permits that object to be recognized, aided by a multiplicity of mental cues. An illustration is a sensory rendering such that the viewer would recognize his own house if it were depicted or remember a landscape that he had once known. Representation abstracts from phenomena only those aspects which conform to accepted systems of scientific explanation. In a scientific image the house is shown as a structure achieved by assembling components, or the landscape is divided into glacial outwash terraces and relict erosion surfaces. Implied in this distinction between illustration and representation is one of the cardinal lessons of science—that the impression of reality conveyed by the senses may be insignificant or illusory and require confirmation or correction by experiment. Goethe's ideal plant and Grew's schematic plant differed in that the former was an illustration only, while the latter was a scientific representation. Both were abstractions from nature, but they referred to widely differing provinces of thought and experience.

Illustrations figure prominently in science, but only as substitutes for direct sensory acquaintance with their objects, as with the frequent use of photographs in publications. For purposes of distinguishing species of organisms, illustrations sometimes serve as well or even better than analytic descriptions, although the latter are confined to those characters that the systematic biologist believes to be diagnostic within their genus. In a painting of insects by Jan van Kessel, the Flemish still-life painter of three centuries ago, one cannot always determine the species of a plant or insect. Where diagnostic characters are ignored, even though the illustration conveys with reasonable success a generalized picture of the organism, it cannot be identified as to species. An illustration conveys scientific information by accident or in a circumscribed sense.

A figure is a representation if it permits its object to be referred to categories

[7] Bichat, *Traité d'anatomie descriptive* . . . , vol. 1 (Paris: Gabon et Cie and Brosson, 1801), pp. xxviii-xxx.
[8] See William Coleman, *Georges Cuvier Zoologist* . . . (Harvard University Press, 1964), reproductions of Cuvier's drawings at pp. 54 and 56.

of value in scientific explanation such as cause and effect, disposition in space and time, or observed sequences of operations. Such representations arise through a process of abstraction which generalizes them in these respects. Thus, the models employed by scientists represent principles of construction or operation. A representation need not present an immediate sensory resemblance to its object. It may be acceptable as a formal substitute for it so long as it exemplifies the class of phenomena to which it refers. Representational imagery often entails a classification or limitation of the objects to which it applies and to which it may be related in any manner properly within the scientific domain. Failing this the figure is at best an illustration.

The distinction between scientific and nonscientific modes of abstraction does not turn upon whether or not the processes of concept formation are visual: for many scientists, powers of visualization have been indispensable in the formulation of hypotheses and the organization of results. Nor is it the case that the scientist abstracts from his experience while the poet works from immediate sense impressions that have not been abstracted. Goethe's visual image of the ideal plant was an illustration because it lacked a scientifically meaningful relation to the processes of plant growth it was intended to represent. The elements of the image could not be matched with the parts of plants as they might have been observed or the processes by which they grew. His notion that the skull was composed of degenerate or fused vertebrae could not have been demonstrated if he had examined a series of the vertebrate skeletons available to him. His schematizations were profoundly satisfying esthetically as his enthusiasm for their translation into poetry showed and the adulation of his contemporaries proved. Goethe's attempts to portray nature were not mistaken because they contained errors of fact but because he disregarded the limits of scientific evidence. In effect, he denied that scientific knowledge had to be limited, which is equivalent to denying its validity. The great neurophysiologist Sir Charles Scott Sherrington, who himself wrote poetry and devoted great care to working out his general ideas of nature, delivered in 1942 a Deneke lecture at Oxford on Goethe's view of nature. It is to this idea of nature rather than to science that Goethe's images refer. Nature is fecund and powerful, constantly changing, symbolized by a pantheon of deities unceasingly reshaping the world. "Nature resembled not too distantly a vast Brocken-scene in which the supernatural worked the natural, with Faust as spectator." [9] Goethe's nature is orphic after the fashion of the Greek mysteries, and man's greatest privilege is to know her awesome beauty. Through her votary the poet, Nature becomes known, as in the *Urworte* poems of 1817, which appeared in the second volume of his morphology.[10]

[9] Sherrington, *Goethe on Nature & on Science* (1942), p. 27.
[10] For a translation and interpretation of these poems, see Elizabeth Sewell, *The Orphic Voice* (1960), pp. 269-275.

Goethe acted as though nature was in essence so beautiful as to be inaccessible to ordinary scientific procedures. In so doing he dissociated esthetics from science. By requiring great generality and regularity in images of nature, he placed them beyond the validating powers of science. For want of beauty he forsook scientific representations, seeking instead universally generalized illustrations which could answer to his intuitions. In consequence Goethe repeatedly sacrificed science to his esthetic ideas. But visualizations of organisms, esthetic in character, would gain rapidly in importance in the scientific representation of organisms in the decades following his death.

The pursuit of an unattainable ideal form was the central intellectual enterprise of Romantic nature philosophy, of which Goethe's morphology is but one example. Johann Gottfried Herder (1744-1803), poet, critic, and early student of languages and anthropology, insistently stressed the unity of all forms of life. His principal work, *Outlines of a Philosophy of the History of Man* (1784-1791), states his view that all living beings were created according to a single plan common to them all. Friedrich Schelling (1775-1854), while primarily a philosopher whose writings expounded the doctrine that nature and spirit existed objectively in an identical substratum, sought also to apply this notion to scientific subjects. This led him to absurd speculations set forth in inflated jargon in his books *Ideas of a Philosophy of Nature* (1797) and *On the Soul of the World* (1798), wherein he presented endless statements of identity: among all physical forces, of matter and energy, of subjective and objective experience, of mind and magnetism, and of matter and spirit. Hegel (1770-1831), who had been a childhood friend and student of Schelling, criticized his notions in a memorable passage in the foreword of his *Phenomenology of Spirit* (1807), describing them as the "simplicity of the emptiness of knowledge; a night in which all cows are black."

Lorenz Oken (1779-1851) expounded the idealistic morphology in his *Textbook of Naturphilosophie* (1809-11), in which some of its primary doctrines received their clearest statement. The geometrical basis of *Naturphilosophie* is made explicit in his statement "The sphere is, therefore, the most perfect form; for it is the primary, the divine form. Angular forms are imperfect. The more spherical a thing is in form, by so much more perfect and divine is it. The inorganic is angular, the organic spherical."[11] The organism is that which combines all of the activities of the universe within a single individual body. His inaugural discourse upon becoming professor at Jena in 1807 was devoted to the notion that "the head is none other than a vertebral column" and that the skull consisted of four modified elemental vertebrae, a "discovery" that Goethe sought to claim as his own. He was particularly impressed by the spiral structures in the vessels of plants, a subject that also exerted a lifelong fascination for Goethe. Oken wrote that spirals were found more frequently in the higher plants than

[11] Oken, *Elements of Physiophilosophy* (1847), p. 29.

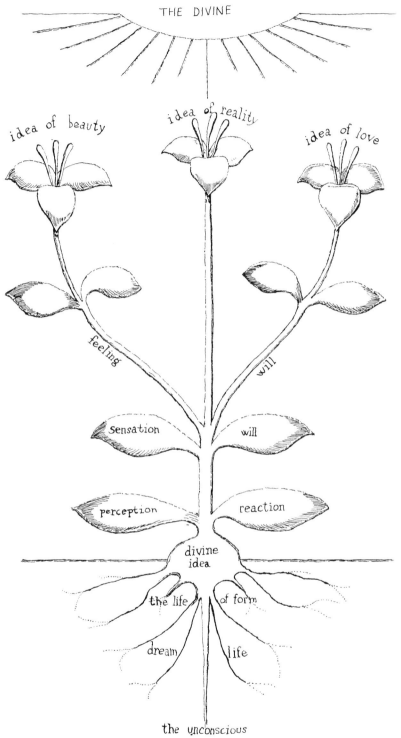

Figure 3. The plant form as an emblem of the human sensibility. (After Carus, *Natur und Idee,* Leipzig: Wilhelm Braumüller, 1861, following p. 459.)

in mushrooms or lichens, while ferns have only a single bundle of spiral vessels. These speculations were further elaborated by the botanist Nees von Esenbeck (1776-1858), who was highly regarded for his detailed studies of tropical floras. His *Textbook of Botany* (1820-1821) is a thicket of mystic identities and polarities in which it appears that the entire vegetative world is one mighty leaf. Fungi represent the north; vascular plants, the south; animals, the midnight; and man, the noon.

The intermingling of esthetic presuppositions with biological speculation is well exemplified in the work of Carl Gustav Carus (1789-1869), professor of anatomy in Dresden and later court physician to the king of Saxony. He was a versatile and learned man, a close friend of Goethe, an accomplished scientist, a speculative psychologist, but also a man of pronounced esthetic leanings who became well known as a landscape painter. His best-known work is *Psyche* (1846), wherein he presented his ideas on man's unconscious faculties. In his treatise *Nature and Idea* he provided a visual interpretation of the plant as symbol for man's mental life, showing a plant growing toward the sun of God out of the roots of unconsciousness (*Figure 3*).

He shared the aspirations of Goethe and Oken for an ideal unity of plan among animals and wrote that the cranium is "an integral but highly developed portion of the vertebral column" which "is composed of individual vertebrae."[12] His work on comparative anatomy includes two hundred figures drawn by himself which are straightforward representations of organisms and do not betray the embellishment of the artist (*Figure 4*). As a painter, Carus was self-taught. He painted landscapes in oils and completed numerous sketches from 1812 on, works that are accomplished in technique and highly naturalistic. He was fond of depicting mood in nature, as in a dramatic representation of Fingal's Cave seen across a raging sea.[13]

Idealistic natural philosophy spread beyond Germany in the nineteenth century. The French zoologist Geoffroy St. Hilaire (1772-1844) based his extensive work in comparative anatomy on the doctrine of an ideal fundamental type. When he became embroiled in controversy with less speculative scientists who demonstrated the falsity of his assertions, Goethe, in his last year of life, came eagerly to his defense. William Stuart McLeay (1792-1865), an English

---

[12] Carus, *An Introduction to the Comparative Anatomy of Animals* . . . , trans. R. T. Gore (London: Longman, Rees, Orme, Brown, and Green, 1827), vol. I, p. 127. Also Rudolph Zaunick, "Oken, Carus, Goethe: Zur Geschichte des Gedankens der Wirbel-Metamorphose," in *Festgabe Georg Sticker, Historische Studien und Skizzen zu Natur- und Heilwissenschaft* (Berlin: Julius Springer, 1930), pp. 118-129.

[13] Eckart von Sydow, "Carl Gustav Carus und das Naturbewusstsein der romantischen deutschen Malerei," *Monatshefte für Kunstwissenschaft,* vol. 15 (May 1922), pp. 31-39 and 2 pls. Also on Carus, see Carl Haeberlin, "Der Arzt Carl Gustav Carus und Goethe . . . ," *Jahrbuch der Goethe-Gesellschaft* (Weimar), vol. 13 (1927), pp. 184-204, and Reinout Bakker, *Het Wijsgerig en Psychologisch Denken van Carl Gustav Carus* . . . (Utrecht: Vesta, 1954), with a summary in English.

and Australian writer on systematic biology, published elaborate conjectural systems based on an idealized pattern of concentric circles. Each kingdom or order in nature was depicted as a circle enclosing five smaller circles, each of which was similarly divided, and he sought to classify organisms accordingly. *Naturphilosophie* was a leading influence on the work of anatomists and biologists from 1790 to 1830, principally through conferring special standing upon ideal forms.

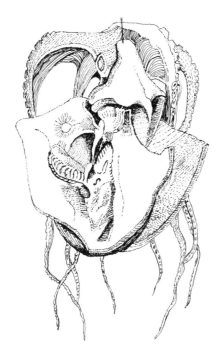

Figure 4. Commencement of the dissection of an octopus. (After Carus, *op. cit.* [fn. 12], pl. 4: fig. 1.)

Oken's statement that spherical forms were characteristic of life while angular forms were imperfect implied a distinction between the complex shapes of living things and the geometrical order of crystal structure. Felix Vicq d'Azyr (1748-1789), a highly accomplished investigator of anatomy and an eminent physician, had argued strongly against drawing analogies between crystal structure and organic bodies. For over a century, branching crystals had been grown in solutions and had been exhibited as "stone plants" as evidence confirming mechanical explanations of plant growth such as those offered by Nehemiah Grew. The use of this figure by Pierre Maupertuis in 1744 has been called "the first occasion on which a nonliving phenomenon has been appealed to as an illustration of what went on in [a] living body." [14] The Romantic nature philosophers attributed to organisms special powers of life which could not be bound by the mechanical

[14] Joseph Needham, *A History of Embryology,* 2nd ed. (Cambridge University Press, 1959), p. 219. Robert Hooke found the *arbor Dianae* of dendritic silver an admirable representation of plant growth in 1665; Daniel Coxe in 1674 and John Beaumont in 1676 had written to similar effect.

regularities exhibited in mineral crystals. But within the mineral kingdom analytical morphology was able to explain achieved structure by the simple juxtaposition of uniform elements whose figure was constant and determinate. This was the basis of the molecular theory of crystallization put forth by Jean Baptiste Romé de l'Isle (1736-1790) in his *Crystallographie* in 1783 and placed on a mathematical basis by Abbé René Just Haüy (1743-1822) in 1801 (*Figure 5*).

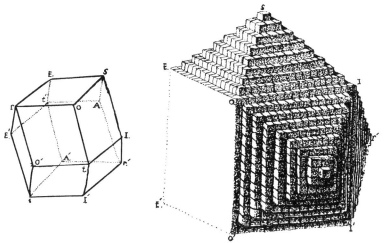

Figure 5. Construction of a dodecahedron with rhombic faces by the addition of regular lamellae to a cubic nucleus. (After Haüy, *Traité de minéralogie . . .* , Paris: 1801, vol. V, pl. 2: figs. 11 and 13.)

Haüy discovered that the form of crystals was limited by faces whose relation to one another was strictly regular. Thus, for example, a crystal with a pentagonal cross-section cannot exist, as a five-fold axis of symmetry cannot be reduced to rational numbers. The variety of possible symmetry groups in crystals proved to be limited in number to thirty-two. The demonstration that the classic geometrical solids existed in mineral crystals was a brilliant and inspiring confirmation of the operation of mechanical laws in nature.[15] But the Romantic nature philosophy held that organic life transcended relationships that could be expressed mathematically. The science of crystallography introduced a distinction between the living and the nonliving, an aspect of the idea that organisms had distinctive characteristics of form which separated them from nonliving nature, an idea of organic form.

[15] See the excellent study by John G. Burke, *Origins of the Science of Crystals* (1966); also Polanyi, *Personal Knowledge* (1964), pp. 43-48. The eminent crystallographer J. D. Bernal notes that the symmetry of crystals and molecular aggregates arises from the geometrical apposition of equal parts, as distinguished from the symmetry properties of formed organisms, which he considers to be generated primarily by equal times of growth. "Symmetry of the Genesis of Form" (1966).

Esthetics and II
Analogies to Life

Samuel Taylor Coleridge's poem *The Ancient Mariner* (1798) comes to a climax at the moment of the mariner's vivid awareness of beauty in the "rich attire" of the water-snakes and elegance in their tracks of "golden fire," where before he had been repelled by the appearance of the "million million slimy things." The recognition of beauty is the central symbolic occurrence in Romantic poetry. Indeed the greatest achievement of the Romantic Movement was to analyze the experience of beauty. This accomplishment required a philosophical approach to esthetic experience. In this endeavor also Coleridge played a leading role, and organic form figures as largely in his conception of beauty in art as it had in the central event of his poem. That this was true was in large measure due to Coleridge's own philosophical interests in biology and his acquaintance with continental theories of esthetics, gained during a German tour with the Wordsworths in 1798 and 1799.

In a number of lectures and essays, of which the most important was "On the Definitions of Life" (1830), Coleridge criticized empirical physiologists as pursuing too narrow an approach to the problems of life. They studied organisms as though they were simple physico-chemical assemblages, a piece at a time, while the most important phenomena of life resided at the level of the organism as a whole and could be understood only by the exercise of comprehensive powers of insight. While Coleridge did not propose an extra-scientific speculative approach, he readily saw the inadequacies of a stepwise analytic method. A machine could best be understood by taking it apart, but the dissection of an organism yielded members whose meaning was lost when they were removed from the intact body. Only the elementary powers of the mind were required to design a machine or to analyze the structure of a crystal. But to understand the organism the mind must project something of itself into nature, perceive with its highest integrative powers, and reshape the raw sensations of experience. This, in Coleridge's celebrated conception, was the faculty of imagination.[1]

Coleridge maintained that the imagination was an active shaping faculty. He exalted its creativity above the routine processing of information. In the eighteenth century a materialistic school of writers on psychological subjects had supposed that patterns of perception and ideas generally arose through the combination of more elementary sensations or rudiments. This was the theory of the association of ideas. The Romantic stress on imagination served to counter a simplistic notion of mind very much like that of twentieth-century writers who suppose that the electronic computer offers an adequate representation of human mentality. Thus we find Coleridge writing in March of 1801:

Newton was a mere materialist—*Mind* in his system is always *passive*—a lazy Looker-on in an external world. . . . Any system built on the passiveness of the mind must be false as a system.[2]

This criticism of Newton, while reminiscent of William Blake, was probably based on some of the early speculative ideas of the chemist Humphrey Davy (1778-1829).

Coleridge befriended Davy on a visit to Bristol in October of 1799 and they often visited each other over the next ten years. Davy became the most eminent English scientist of the first three decades of the nineteenth century, widely celebrated as a genius. In the best Romantic manner, his handsome countenance overwhelmed fashionable audiences at the Royal Institution. In his youth he wrote a fervid essay "In Defence of Materialism," which reminds us of Shelley, and, as Wordsworth did, he penned verses describing aspirations for scientific knowledge:

> To scan the laws of Nature, to explore
> The tranquil reign of mild Philosophy;
> Or on Newtonian wings sublime to soar
> Through the bright regions of the starry sky.[3]

[1] I. A. Richards, *Coleridge on Imagination* (London: Kegan Paul, Trench, Trubner, 1934).
[2] Letter to Thomas Poole, in E. L. Griggs, ed., *Collected Letters of Samuel Taylor Coleridge,* vol. 2 (Oxford: Clarendon Press, 1956), no. 388. Also see Gordon McKenzie, *Organic Unity in Coleridge* (1939).
[3] "The Sons of Genius," in John Davy, *Memoirs of the Life of Sir Humphry Davy, Bart.* . . . , in *The Collected Works* . . . , vol. 1 (London: Smith, Elder, 1839), pp. 24-26.

Davy and Coleridge used to inhale nitrous oxide for its hallucinatory effects as they walked on the banks of the Severn River composing poetry by moonlight. There had been some thought that Davy, who had contributed to Southey's *Annual Anthology,* might write a poem for the second edition of *Lyrical Ballads,* for which he superintended the printing in 1800. Davy overcame his fondness for speculation while still a young man, and in his prime he was one of the most rigorous exponents of the experimental method. But he took the same position as Coleridge regarding the character of the imagination, repudiating the notion "that the imagination ought to be passive in physical research."[4]

Imagination, as well as reason, is necessary to perfection in the philosophical mind. A rapidity of combination, a power of perceiving analogies, and of comparing them by facts, is the creative source of discovery. Discrimination and delicacy of sensation, so important in physical research, are other words for taste; and the love of nature is the same passion, as the love of the magnificent, the sublime, and the beautiful.[5]

The powers of imagination transcended those of the mere association of ideas just as the living organism showed higher powers than those required for the aggregation of molecular units into crystals. The creative imagination finds, in Coleridge's words, "correspondences and symbols" in the growth of a plant, as it changes nutritive elements into its own substance during growth. Before a living plant, he wrote, "I feel an awe, as if there were before my eyes the same power as that of the reason." Edward Young's *Conjectures on Original Composition* (1759) had distinguished original creations from imitations by employing an organic analogy for the creative imagination: "An *Original* may be said to be of a *vegetable* nature; it rises spontaneously from the vital root of genius; it *grows,* it is not *made.*"[6] A number of German writers stressed the organic character of imaginative creation, especially the linguist, translator, and critic August Wilhelm von Schlegel (1767-1845). In his Berlin lectures on literature he stated that art, "creating autonomously like nature, both organized and organizing, must form living works, which are first set in motion, not by an outside mechanism, like a pendulum, but by an indwelling power . . . ."[7] Goethe several times likened his own development as a poet to the growth and flowering of a plant.

The creative power of the imagination was symbolized by the growing plant; the critic and historian Meyer Abrams has called this the theory of vegetable

[4] Lecture of 1811 in *Works* . . . , vol. 8 (1840), p. 317.

[5] Davy, "Parallels between Art and Science" [1807], p. 208.

[6] Young, *Conjectures on Original Composition,* ed. Edith J. Morley (Manchester University Press, 1918), p. 7.

[7] Schlegel, *Vorlesungen über schöne Litteratur und Kunst,* pt. I (1801-1802), in R. Seuffert, ed., "Deutsche Litteraturdenkmale . . . ," vol. 17 (Heilbron: Gebr. Henninger, 1884), p. 102.

genius.[8] It probably originated from the belief, whose history I have traced elsewhere, that plants enjoyed sensation, feeling, and other attributes of animal life.[9] This exaggerated estimate of the faculties of plants was very widespread in the eighteenth century. It is perhaps most strikingly set forth in the extravagant speculative poems of Erasmus Darwin (1731-1802), wherein plants were personified as passionate lovers and endowed with all the powers of animals. Here, as an example, is his versified account of the metamorphosis of plants:

> Closed in the *Style* the tender pith shall end,
> The lengthening Wood in circling *Stamens* bend;
> The smoother *Rind* its soft embroidery spread
> In vaulted *Petals* o'er their fertile bed;
> While the rough *Bark,* in circling mazes roll'd,
> Forms the green *Cup* with many a wrinkled fold;[10]

That biological materials were deemed suitable for use in poetry was a consequence of the organic concept of imagination. In his essay "On Poesy or Art" (1818) Coleridge wrote that the visual image of nature was "fitted to the limits of the human mind," enabling it to elicit from natural forms moral reflections and serving "to make the external internal, the internal external, to make nature thought, and thought nature,—this is the mystery of genius in the Fine Arts."[11]

The poetry of John Keats (1795-1821), which Whitehead once called an example of literature untouched by science, is indeed free of Darwin's didactic explicitness but shows a profound sense of affinity with organic process. The literary scholar Bernard Blackstone has drawn a parallel between the urn, the human work of art, and the fruit, swollen by genial growth. This was Keats' "vast idea," as he called it in *Sleep and Poetry* (1818), "The end and aim of Poesy." Also in this poem he wrote of "the small Breath of new buds unfolding." The swelling of organic forms is a recurrent feature of Keats' poetry, abundantly suggestive of the culminating symbol of the experience of beauty, the Grecian Urn. Blackstone points out that the two volumes of Erasmus Darwin's *Botanic Garden* had opened in 1789 with drawings of cross-sections of flowers and concluded in 1791 with engravings (by William Blake) of the Portland Vase. "The road between traverses, for both poets, the realm of Flora and old Pan. It is

---

[8] Abrams, *The Mirror and the Lamp* (1953). Charles Nicolle, Nobel Laureate in Medicine in 1928, sought to trace all human creativity to biological sources in *Biologie de l'invention* (1932).

[9] "The Super-Life of Plants," in Ritterbush, *Overtures to Biology* (1964), pp. 141-157.

[10] Darwin, *The Botanic Garden, Part I. Containing the Economy of Vegetation. A Poem. With Philosophical Notes.* (London: J. Johnson, 1791), Canto IV. Cf. Carl Linnaeus, "Prolepsis Plantarum" [1763], *Amoenitates Academicae* (Leyden), vol. 6 (1764), pp. 365-383.

[11] In J. Shawcross, ed., *Biographia Literaria* (Oxford: Clarendon Press, 1907), vol. II, pp. 253-254, 258.

adorned with flowers and fruits and corn and branching trees, haunted by spirits of the four elements; it passes over caves bright with crystals and veins of gold and silver ore."[12]

The developing plant form shows relations in time, as it grows, and in space, as it changes its disposition; Keats continually makes explicit reference to these:

> the sweet buds which with a modest pride
> Pull droopingly, in slanting curve aside,
> Their scantly leaved, and finely tapering stems,
>   —"I stood tip-toe . . . ," (1817)

The dynamic tensions of growth, the directions of axes, and the tapering stem exemplify Keats' discernment of the forms elaborated through growth and flowering. Fruiting, in concert with the sun, will "load and bless with fruit the vines," "swell the gourd," "plump the hazel shells/with a sweet kernel." The warmth of autumn will bring late flower to bud "for the bees,/Until they think warm days will never cease,/For summer has o'erbrimm'd their clammy cells." As in Goethe's idea of metamorphosis we find a rhythmic succession from concentration in the seed to the swelling of growth and the climax of efflorescence ("The leap of buds into ripe flowers") until all is distilled into compact fruit. The process of determinate growth proceeds, as does the faculty of song, by "bringing shapes from the invisible world." And so Keats wrote that "if Poetry comes not as naturally as the Leaves to a tree it had better not come at all."

Coleridge defined a true work of art as that which displays the characteristics of an organism rather than a mechanical device. His distinction between mechanical and organic form was stated as follows:

The form is mechanic when on any given material we impress a pre-determined form, not necessarily arising out of the properties of the material, as when to a mass of wet clay we give whatever shape we wish it to retain when hardened. The organic form, on the other hand, is innate; it shapes as it develops itself from within, and the fullness of its development is one and the same with the perfection of its outward form. Such is the life, such the form. Nature, the prime genial artist, inexhaustible in diverse powers, is equally inexhaustible in forms. Each exterior is the physiognomy of the being within, its true image reflected and thrown out from the concave mirror.[13]

Organic forms were defined by five attributes repeatedly stated by Coleridge. Of great consequence for the future, they are well worth noting. First, the origin of the whole precedes the differentiation of the parts. The whole is primary; the parts are derived. In the organic form "the whole is everything

---

[12] Blackstone, *The Consecrated Urn* (1959), p. 337. See Hambridge, *Dynamic Symmetry* (1920), for an analysis of the organic symmetry properties of Greek vases.
[13] In T. M. Raysor, ed., *Coleridge's Shakespearean Criticism* (London: Constable, 1930), vol. I, p. 224; see also pp. 4, 5.

and the parts are nothing."[14] "Whatever is truly organic and living, the whole is prior to the parts."[15] An organic form will be one that conveys this property of its genesis to its beholders. Second, the form manifests the process of growth by which it arose. "Productivity" or growth is the first power of living things, and it exhibits itself as "evolution and extension in the Plant."[16] The organic form proclaims itself as the end result of a progressive sequence of development. Third, as it grows the plant assimilates diverse elements into its own substance:

Events and images, the lively and spirit-stirring machinery of the external world, are like light, and air, and moisture, to the seed of the Mind, which would else rot and perish. In all processes of mental evolution the objects of the senses must stimulate the Mind; and the Mind must in turn assimilate and digest the food which it thus receives from without.[17]

Fourth, the achieved form of the plant is directed from within, as Coleridge observed in the quotation above. The external aspect of living things is determined by internal processes, not, as in a human artifact, from without. Fifth, the parts of the living whole are interdependent. As Abrams puts it, "Imaginative unity is an *organic* unity: a self-evolved system, constituted by a living interdependence of parts, whose identity cannot survive their removal from the whole."

Coleridge developed the concept of organic form out of an analysis of Shakespeare's plays, which he held to have been designed from a unified view of human nature. Each play was organic because part and whole were interdependent and informed by a single conception of man's place in nature, and also because the subject matter was well adapted to the dramatic purpose. Having found these formal qualities, which satisfied the criteria for organic form, Coleridge was able to praise the work of art manifesting them as a genuine product of the imagination. On just the same grounds Friedrich Schlegel had praised Goethe's novel *Wilhelm Meister* as a perfectly organic work of art, wherein the parts repeated the whole and all elements were interdependent.[18]

Romantic writers on questions of esthetics displayed a unity of aim and certain themes were common to their works to a degree that has been unknown since. Yet to speak of a synthesis among these writers may be to use too strong a word. Goethe could never acquiesce in Kant's subjectivism, for example. But by comparison with the proliferation of doctrines arising in the following century, the

[14] In T. Ashe, ed., *The Table Talk and Omniana of Samuel Taylor Coelridge* (London: G. Bell and Sons, 1923), p. 145 [December 18, 1831].
[15] In Kathleen Coburn, ed., *The Philosophical Lectures of Samuel Taylor Coleridge Hitherto Unpublished* (New York: Philosophical Library, 1949), p. 196 [January 18, 1819].
[16] "Monologues by the Late Samuel Taylor Coleridge, Esq. No. I: Life," *Fraser's Magazine for Town and Country*, vol. 12 (1835), p. 495.
[17] Alice D. Snyder, ed., *S. T. Coleridge's Treatise on Method . . .* (London: Constable, 1934), p. 7.
[18] In Jakob Minor, ed., *Friedrich Schlegel: Seine prosaischen Jugendschriften* (Vienna: C. Konegen, 1906), vol. 2.

esthetic philosophies of Kant, Goethe, the idealists, and Coleridge seem to represent a convergence at least on a few central questions. The organic character of the process of artistic creation, its affinity with the generative forces of living nature, was commonly asserted. Where formal properties in a work of art were praised they most frequently were attributes shared with organisms as they were then understood. Indeed, as we shall see later on, the properties Coleridge deemed organic became guiding principles that influenced the course of development of biological science.

Having referred to form in natural objects and works of art, I should indicate the sense in which I use the word. With natural objects form means shape—the magnitude and boundaries of the object or the disposition of its component elements in space. Form must be abstracted from the object in order to be portrayed, even where the result is a simple figure in plane geometry. In Aristotelian philosophy, form implied a determining principle that shaped matter—a meaning I have sought to avoid in this discussion. In works of art, form must also be abstracted, but rarely in so direct a manner as with natural objects. The facile antithesis of form and content in a work is not satisfying conceptually, nor is form to be identified with the artist's plan for his work. Form in a work of art is the totality of relationships among the elements of which a work of art is composed. Most simply, it is the surface of a solid piece of sculpture. It is the metrical structure of a poem, its rhyme scheme, and all of the rhythmic sequences —oral, graphic, cognitive, and symbolic—that it contains. Form is the mode of disposition of the visual aspect of a painting, not simply shapes but scale, tension, balance, distribution, and discontinuities in texture or color. Form is usually abstracted from a work of art for purposes of reference to an esthetic principle; where it does so the form may be said to be a representation of the work. Form should not be understood as a simple matter of structure or geometry.

In the system of Friedrich W. J. Schelling (1775-1854) art and science were seen as virtually identical strivings after knowledge of an ultimate reality. The shapes of sculpture are prototypes of the form of organisms. Music represents the composer's sense of the rhythm of the universe. The artist reverts to a subconscious stratum where man and nature are one. One of the most remarkable statements of the ready accessibility of expressive experience through organic form is the poet's dream in the fifth book of Wordsworth's *The Prelude* (1805-06), in which a mysterious figure presents to his view a rough stone and says it is Euclid's *Elements,* representing simple geometry. Then the figure holds up "a Shell/Of a surpassing brightness" and says "this Book/Is something of more worth." The figure stretched forth the shell, "so beautiful in shape" and commanded the poet to hold it to his ear:

I did so,
And heard that instant in an unknown Tongue,
Which yet I understood, articulate sounds,

> A loud prophetic blast of harmony,
> An Ode, in passion uttered . . . .   (V, lines 93-97)

These lines are remarkable testimony to the esthetic importance of organic form and it is important that this experience should have been presented as a dream.

Adopted as an organizing idea about the formal, external aspects of works of art, the focus of the concept of organic form gradually shifted toward the unconscious processes of creation which it seemed to represent. Organic concepts of creativity afforded the first satisfactory account of the formative powers of the unconscious. The antithesis between the organic and mechanical applied not only to the outward aspect of works of art but also served to distinguish the spontaneity which responds to inner promptings from the deliberation of conscious methods of artistic creation. In the words of Thomas Carlyle, "The artificial is the conscious mechanical; the natural is the unconscious dynamical. Unconsciousness is the sign of creation, consciousness at best that of manufacture."[19] The organic form may be the direct expression of the unconscious or if it comes from the external world it comes endowed with a special appeal, the capacity to enlist the latent faculties of the human mind. The foundations of the modern sensibility, whether in art or in biological science, were laid in the fifty years between 1780 and 1830. As the nineteenth century progressed, a profusion of doctrines spread out from these earlier premises; naturalism, estheticism, and idealism, to name a few. Hartmann's theory of the unconscious, Nietzsche's biological esthetics, Fechner's experimental esthetics, and Ruskin's theories of beauty trace their origins to the synthesis between the imaginative and objective aspects of visual experience achieved through the idea of organic form. There is little sign of the primary importance of organic form for the advancement of esthetics in the paintings of nineteenth-century artists. The sensuous curves of Art Nouveau were to be its first explicit visual manifestation in art, however numerous its anticipations in Millais' meticulously veined leaves, painted under a hand lens, or Ruskin sprawled out upon the grass, drawing the blades as they grew, "until every square foot of meadow, or mossy bank, became an infinite picture and possession, and the grace and adjustment to each other of growing leaves, a subject of more curious interest to me than the composition of any painter's master-piece."[20]

Because the formal properties of organisms were used to account for esthetic experience in the arts we should note the enhanced status during the Romantic period of the sense of beauty in nature generally. It is a commonplace of the history of taste that toward the end of the eighteenth century there was a heightening of the experience of beauty in nature. More important for our

---

[19] Quoted by G. Kepes, *The New Landscape* (1956), p. 193.
[20] Quoted from a notebook of the year 1847-1848 by E. T. Cook, *The Life of John Ruskin* (London: George Allen, 1911), vol. I, p. 218.

present purpose, esthetic theory kept pace with the deepening sensibility. In 1790 Immanuel Kant (1724-1804) published the *Critique of Judgment,* in which he dealt with the ultimately esthetic character of the presuppositions underlying man's knowledge of the world. Man experiences beauty in certain aspects of nature, according to Kant, as a result of properties in his esthetic judgment, and not because beauty is an objective quality inherent in nature. Regularity in the object induces an experience of rhythm in its beholder. The sense that responds to such harmony is within ourselves, but we tend to impute the quality of harmoniousness to the object. The pleasure we experience in contemplating a decorative design does not arise from its utility or our desire to own it but from the pleasurable play of our mental faculties in its presence. Nature exhibits "purposiveness without purpose," an apparent orderliness that men enjoy, although there is no rational basis for supposing any actual designing intelligence. The sense of beauty works in all men through a principle of subjective universality; a beautiful object should be so for everyone who sees it.

The beauty of the nightingale's song derives from its existence in nature; if a boy hides in a bush and pipes the notes, they lose their fascination for us as soon as the fraud is discovered.[21] Nature is beautiful because it offers "a highly satisfactory fitting of experience precisely to our faculty of experiencing, to the progress of our knowledge."[22] Men know the world through sight. It is simply common sense to base one's understanding upon order where it is perceived. Form is that quality of objects which will be perceived alike by all men. Thus, harmony and symmetry provide foretastes of knowledge yet to come, even though Kant did not believe that scientific knowledge could be gained in this way. When a regularity is perceived in nature, it gives rise to an esthetic feeling of pleasure auspicious for knowledge. The sense of beauty is the light shadow cast by the cooperation of all parties to the fact of knowledge.

Kant's philosophy thus provides systematic insight into the process whereby the esthetic judgment—through the medium of a visual representation—may serve to guide the cognitive faculty to a superior scientific understanding of its object. The more beautiful a representation is, the greater an understanding it may reveal of its object. "Nature is beautiful," he wrote, "because it looks like Art; and Art can only be called beautiful if we are conscious of it as Art while

[21] *Kant's Kritik of Judgment* [1790], I, §42. It is helpful to be reminded that the area in which Kant was willing to apply his theory of beauty was strictly circumscribed and that his ideas took on greater generality in the writings of others, especially Coleridge (E. F. Carritt, *The Theory of Beauty* [1928], pp. 63-81). For the place of Kant's ideas in the history of concepts of design in nature see Clarence Glacken's masterful summary, *Traces on the Rhodian Shore* (1967), pp. 530-37.

[22] William K. Wimsatt, *Literary Criticism: A Short History* (New York: Knopf, 1957), p. 371.

yet it looks like Nature."[23] The visual representation of phenomena may thus be expected to offer special advantages to the understanding. We may suppose that if biological science could harness the sense of beauty, instead of ostracizing it in the much castigated *Naturphilosophie,* man's knowledge of nature could thereafter progress through dialectical interplay between intuitions of order and observations of the organisms themselves. The esthetic of organic form was ideally suited to serve as the program for an exhilarating course of discovery which would lead to the ultimate foundations of organic form in the world of nature.

I designate as the idea of organic form the system of beliefs originating with F. Schlegel, Schelling, and Coleridge, that form in living beings is more complex than form in nonliving nature and that the form of living organisms or their remains is a property of the whole, while in nonliving entities form results from the disposition of the parts of which they are composed. The interdependence of part and whole was the principal element of novelty in the idea of organic form, by which it represented a departure from the continuity principle of the great scale of being, according to which organisms had of course been recognized as "higher" than inert substances. The idea receives its primary statement in terms of the science of morphology, but its direct corollary in esthetics is that art embodies discrete formal properties that are peculiar to organisms, wherein they differ from inanimate matter. This concept goes beyond Aristotelian unity of structure by recognizing affinities between the artistic imagination and biological process. Goethe exemplified the idea of organic form in his work and in his views on creativity and to some extent in his morphological writings. The Romantic nature philosophy centered upon the idea of form rather than representations of forms as they objectively existed in organisms. The progress of biology in the nineteenth century resulted largely from the pursuit of a program of investigation whereby the esthetic presuppositions of the idea of organic form were shown to be applicable to the scientific study of organisms. In the two chapters that follow I shall seek to show that the science of biology has been guided by considerations of orderliness, reflecting the influence of the idea of organic form and constantly revalidated by reference to empirical reality.

[23] Kant, *op. cit,* I, § 45.   Michael Polanyi, *Personal Knowledge* [1958], ch. 6, distinguishes the quality of intellectual "beauty" in a theory from "elegance," a term that he uses only for formal, mathematical constructs. A representation can only be beautiful when it is believed to be true, he concludes.

III

A Tissue of Imagining

THE CONCEPT OF organic form originated as a literary esthetic principle but became a primary guiding idea in biology, where it was attended with numerous consequences. The influence of the idea of organic form shows the fertile play of the esthetic factor in scientific fields such as biology whose content is highly visual. Nowhere is this more clearly shown than in the study of the structure of the tissues of organisms.

Each of the ideal elements that Goethe supposed to make up the structure of plants manifested the powers of the whole. There was no suggestion that the organism in its entirety possessed qualities differing from those of its components, the ideal leaf or the ideal vertebra in animals. Lorenz Oken thought that organisms were composed of "monads" within each of which were conjoined gravity, magnetism, and "electrism," a combination resulting in galvanism, the essential power of life. In his system whatever is galvanic is truly organic. "Galvanism lies at the basis of all the processes of the organic world. They are either modifications of it, or only its combinations with other and still higher actions." [1] Whatever shows the power of motion is an indivisible

[1] See "Electricity: The Soul of the Universe," in Ritterbush, *Overtures to Biology* (1964), pp. 15-56.

organism. The smallest self-moving entities are "infusoria"—a term then in use for microscopic organisms generally, but Oken meant the smallest specks of life in which the combination of fundamental forces could occur. Every plant and animal was made up of these "infinitely numerous mucus points . . . infusorial vesicles, that by different combinations assume different forms, and grow up into higher organisms."[2] A tree could not be considered to be an individual but was instead an aggregation of "innumerable fascicles," each endowed with the qualities of life. The experimental physiologists of the day were equally at a loss to account for phenomena of nutrition, growth, and reproduction, and generally restricted their inquiries to vital phenomena presenting analogies to more familiar chemical processes. The science of biology had become polarized into two divergent schools of thought with radically different views of form in organisms. To the *Naturphilosophen* form was an ideal and ultimately nonscientific aspect of life while to the physiologists it was an irrelevance. From the idea of organic form were drawn contributions, both esthetic and scientific, which were principally responsible for resolving this crippling divergence of attitude and approach.

The sphere was the most nearly ideal of the forms of transcendental morphology and, according to that system of beliefs, its shape served to distinguish living nature from crystal growth. Whatever manifested the spherical form was alive. In living bodies made up of such elegant elements the whole form would clearly be more complex than that of its parts, but the ideal elements would exist, nonetheless, beyond the range of unaided vision, where their presence could be detected only with the microscope. Oken had hinted at a globular construction for living matter in saying that the intersection of his three life forces "could only produce the globe." While some animal tissue was made up of points (the nerves), or lines (the muscles), bone would be found to be composed of *globules,* with a tendency to move around the nerves like planets around the sun. Thus arose the spherical shape of the skull, because bone was "the obedient planet of the nerve." The primary mucus of life was also thought to be globular in form.

In 1812 Joseph and Carl Wenzel wrote that the brains of fish, birds, quadrupeds, and man were all made up of globules, "the particular structure of the whole of the cerebrum and nerves," and that similarly shaped corpuscles were the "fundamental structure of all the solid parts without exception."[3] Sir Everard Home, an eminent English anatomist, wrote in 1818 that muscle and nerve fibers were composed of tiny globules joined together in lines.[4] In 1821 he

[2] Oken, *Elements of Physiophilosophy* [1809-1811], p. 190.
[3] Wenzel, *De Penitori Structura Cerebri Hominis et Brutorum* (Tübingen: Cottam, 1812), pp. 27-36.
[4] Home, "In the Changes the Blood Undergoes in the Act of Coagulation," *Philosophical Transactions,* vol. 108 (1818), pp. 172-198.

claimed that the nerves and brain contained innumerable globules between two-and four-thousandths of an inch in size.[5]

According to the comparative anatomist Johann Friedrich Meckel (1781-1833), all organs and fluids of the body were composed of small globules of varying sizes. They were almost never angular but might be elliptical or flattened into the form of discs. These globules and the mucus around them he held to form all organized bodies.[6] In 1823 Henri Milne-Edwards (1800-1885), a Belgian anatomist working in Paris who later conducted meticulous studies of invertebrates, reported that he found globules 1/300 millimeter in diameter in all tissues.[7]

Henri Dutrochet (1776-1847) was a physiologist whose writings on the spiral curve of the motive organ of the sensitive plant delighted Goethe. He proposed that all organisms were composed of spheres—in both fluid and solid parts. All tissues were *organized,* "entirely composed of globular corpuscles." He persuaded himself that blood corpuscles in a tadpole were spherical rather than disc shaped and that the discs reported by Leeuwenhoek and numerous other observers had been errors of interpretation resulting from poor images in their microscopes. Here was the ideal form everywhere in living bodies—plants and animals, solids and fluids—delighting Dutrochet by its occurrence. Almost certainly he was seeing bubbles of air and water in his preparations, with the prominent black borders that surround them in microscopic images. Moreover, certain kinds of brain and nerve tissues form globules if permitted to remain in water! It was Dutrochet who had been deceived by the microscope. When he looked at the nervous tissue of a snail, he found globules everywhere and they resembled those that he thought he saw in the motive tissues of the sensitive plant *Mimosa pudica (Figure 6).*

He supposed that muscle fibers were strings of globules that drew closer together like pearls on a string and then folded when muscles contracted. He even recorded that he had seen the spherical globules move from blood into the surrounding tissue and solidify into its structure. Thus, he sought to account for growth by the "intercalation" of elements. He thought he saw this actually take place in the blood vessels of a tadpole's tail.

Many times I have seen a single globule escape laterally from a blood vessel and move in the [surrounding] transparent tissue . . . with a slowness which strongly con-

[5] Home, "Microscopical Observations on the Following Subjects: —On the Brain and Nerves, Showing That the Materials of Which They Are Composed Exist in the Blood . . . ," *Philosophical Transactions,* vol. 111 (1821), pp. 26-46.

[6] Meckel, *System der vergleichenden Anatomie,* vol. 1 (Halle: Rengerschen Buchhandlung, 1821), pp. 38-43; and *Manual of General, Descriptive, and Pathological Anatomy* [1816-1820], trans. A. Sidney Doane et al. (Philadelphia: Carey and Lea, 1832), vol. I, pp. 22-25.

[7] Milne-Edwards, *"Mémoire sur la structure élémentaire des principaux tissus organiques des animaux"* (1823).

trasts with the rapidity of the circulatory torrent from which it escaped; soon afterward the globule ceases to move and stands fixed in the transparent tissue . . . .[8]

Dutrochet had been led astray by appearances—he had overlooked finer capillaries which had been out of focus, within which the blood corpuscles had circulated more slowly. His later studies ignored the tempting globules and approached the question of growth through careful experiments on osmosis.[9]

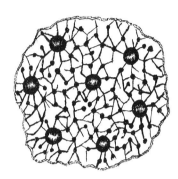 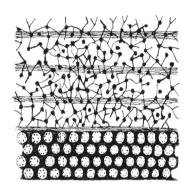

Figure 6. Globules in the "nerve tissue" of plants (left) and animals. (After Dutrochet, *La structure intime des animaux et des végétaux,* 1824, pl. 1: fig. 17 and pl. 2: fig. 21.)

A succession of observers thought they had solved the problem of organic form by finding minute globules in tissues. What they had done was to turn to their microscopes in hopes of fulfilling a program of investigation that started from esthetic premises. They sought some repetitive element, simpler in form than the entire organism, a part subordinate to the whole but still reflecting some essential characteristics. What could be better than the sphere for the perfect fulfillment of this program? The blurred images of their primitive microscopes required interpretation, which the esthetic concept of organic form prompted in the direction of the sphere as a supracrystalline structural component of living substances. Even images in the simple microscope, which Dutrochet praised so highly, were subject to aberrations and in the compound microscopes then in use most elements of the image were surrounded by bewildering halos and "ghosts." The globular structure was a tissue of imaginings.

In 1827 a very thorough search for globules in striated muscles and arterial muscle, as well as in nerves and brains, through the use of an improved microscope of new design, revealed only fibers or irregular masses. It was shown that red corpuscles in human blood were indeed disc shaped, not spherical. As the biologist John Baker has written in his superb articles on the history of the cell

[8] Dutrochet, *Structure intime* (1824), p. 215.
[9] Dutrochet, *Mémoires pour servir a l'histoire anatomique et physiologique des végétaux et des animaux* (Paris: J.-B. Balliére, 1837).

theory, "the particular advantage of [this new] instrument was that spherical aberration was corrected and the 'ring' appearance around small particles thus reduced."[10] The eye had taken unfair advantage of the latitude for interpretation afforded by the microscope. The primary organic form was latent in the minds of those early microanatomists, awaiting the promptings of the imagination to repair the deficiencies in the image of nature provided by the microscope. They had seen with the eye of the poet, which half creates and only half perceives. And in biology as in poetry, when the imagination was given rein, the result was the organic form, hidden realms of microscopic complexity, shapes of a higher order than those of crystals, a whole that was greater than the sum of its parts, imaginary but infinitely suggestive. And what is strangest of all, the esthetic concept was soon afterward found to be objectively true.

The globule theory of organic form was at the very least a pregnant intuition of future discovery and certainly a guiding influence in the development of the cell theory, which took form in the work of Matthias Jacob Schleiden (1804-1881) and Theodor Schwann (1810-1882). Schleiden was professor of botany at Jena from 1838 to 1861. He had chosen science as his profession after an unsuccessful suicide attempt. (Despondent about his unsuccessful career as a lawyer in his native Hamburg, he shot himself through the forehead but survived and went on to take additional doctorates in both philosophy and medicine.) A lucid exponent of modern observational techniques, he was highly impatient with *Naturphilosophie*. It would be his manner of proceeding, he said, "to communicate only facts and their immediate consequences, and not to dream."[11] It had long been known that some parts of plants evinced a cellular structure but it was not generally understood that plant growth comprised the multiplication of cells and that cells organized the performance of the vital functions of the organism. Schleiden observed the development of cells in the embryonal sac of a number of different kinds of plants. He interpreted his observations to indicate that new cells arose as free-floating nuclei in a saccharine liquid suspension and then progressed through intermediate stages to their final size and consistency. He correctly determined that the multiplication of cells occurred through the agency of the nucleus. The primary mode of growth in organisms was "by now cells being deposited upon those already existing"(*Figure 7*). In varying degrees Schleiden had been anticipated by Robert Brown, Charles François Brisseau-Mirbel, and others, but he went beyond them in voicing the uncompromising statement that all growth phenomena were reducible to cellular processes of division, growth, or membrane formation and that the cell was the fundamental basis of structure.

[10] Baker, "Cell Theory" (1948), p. 121. See also the account of Hodgkin and J. J. Lister, "Notice of Some Microscopic Observations of the Blood and Animal Tissues," *Philosophical Magazine*, n.s., vol. 2 (1827), pp. 130-138.
[11] Schleiden, "Contributions to Photogenesis" [1838], p. 249.

Schleiden justly observed that cell theory would become "the foundation of the whole science of morphology." "In all plants, with the exception of the few which consist only of one cell, the form depends upon the manner in which the cells are combined together." [12] Thus, a science of form would be based upon the study of cells, the manner and causes of their combinations, and the sequence of their development into the overall form displayed by the organism.

To Theodor Schwann (1810-1882), working as assistant to Johannes Müller in Bonn and Berlin, it seemed that cells arose by crystallization from the ambient fluid. This investigator is deservedly celebrated as the discoverer of cells in virtually all animal tissues, which he held to confirm a unity of plan between plants and animals. In the title of his treatise of 1839 he refers to the "accordance" of plants and animals in structure and growth *(Figure 8)*. Schwann argued that "the fundamental power of organized bodies resolves into that of the

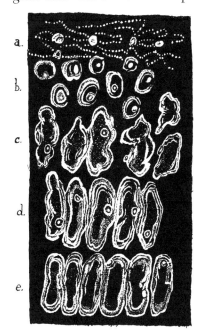
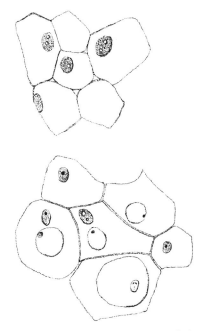

Figure 7. Cellular tissue forming in the plant embryo: *a,* "gum with intermingled mucus [protoplasm] granules and cytoblasts [nuclei]"; *b,* "newly formed cells"; *c-e,* "further development of the cells." (After Schleiden, "Contributions to Phytogenesis" [1838], pl. 1: fig. 1.)

Figure 8. Identity in form between cells and their nuclei in the onion (above) and the notochord of a tadpole (below). (After Schwann, *Accordance in the Structure and Growth of Animals and Plants* [1839], pl. 1: figs. 1 and 4.) For the background of the idea of affinity between plants and animals, see "The Triumph of Botanical Analogy" in Ritterbush, *Overtures to Biology* (1964), pp. 109-157.

[12] Schleiden, *Scientific Botany* [1842], p. 135.

fundamental powers of the individual cells." He sought to argue that all organic capacities stemmed from the structure of the cells (plastic phenomena) or from the chemistry of processes occurring within or around them, for which he coined the term "metabolic phenomena." He took a radical position on the question of the nature of life, insisting that vital phenomena consisted only of chemical operations or plastic processes directly analogous to crystallization. This was a familiar materialistic notion, but, as codiscoverer of the cell theory, Schwann was able to confer great scientific authority upon the attitude that life was ultimately reducible to physics and chemistry and that there would not be found in living things any vital energy *sui generis* or a formative principle. The controversy between "mechanists" and "vitalists" was greatly intensified, and arguments over the validity of such statements have continued ever since. It does not explain vital phenomena simply to attribute the capacity to generate the orderliness of living systems to small particles of nonliving matter without indicating how they exercise their formative influence. Nor should one expect that physical sciences, developed to explain particular categories of phenomena, are infinitely extensible to all of nature. Eugene Wigner, the theoretical physicist, has pointed out the flaw in such reasoning. He observes that concepts which prove adequate to describe natural phenomena are rarely those which have been developed through prior study of much more restricted phenomena, although he acknowledges that the development of new concepts often begins with the uncritical application of old ones.[13] The soundest approach seems to be that which aims to determine and explain the properties that an organism manifests at each level of its organization, from the molecule, the cell, and the intact organism to the populations of which it is a part. To the higher hierarchical levels of this sequence physical processes of crystallization offer no analogy.

Whatever its philosophical validity, the reductionist attitude has been a fertile source of discovery in biology and counts among its exponents a conspicuous majority of biochemists today. Often it is expressed as the proposition that the forms of organisms may be reduced to principles of order inherent in chemistry or physics, the antithesis of the idea of organic form, but to an equal degree a principle of esthetics, bespeaking a different concept of order. Because the mechanist and vitalist positions are ultimately reducible to attitudes toward what has not yet been discovered, they are unsatisfactory as classifiers of scientific accomplishment. The label tells us not what a scientist actually discovered or stated but only where he was looking when he did it or what he made of it. As Everett Mendelsohn, a leading student of this subject, has said,

What this means for the historian is that he must look not only at the professions of "faith" made by the scientists, but also at the theories constructed and the relative

[13] Review of Francis Crick, *Of Molecules and Men* (1966), in *Science,* vol. 150 (May 12, 1967), pp. 798-99.

importance of their various components and come away not using the simple classifications of *mechanism* and *vitalism*, but instead present an analysis of the explanatory
models, suggesting which were the critical and which were the expendable components
and where possible indicating the way in which the concept was understood by
contemporary investigators.[14]

It is my contention that the history of biology cannot be understood without
reference to the development and the scientific and esthetic standing of images
which have been held to represent living things scientifically. These are visually realized constructs for the theories, and the historian interprets them in
the manner which Mendelsohn suggests that nonvisual models should be com-
prehended. Incidentally, the primacy of visual knowledge in the cognitive processes of the science of biology is an insuperable obstacle to Marshall MacLuhan's
flaccid assertion that the sense of sight has a fixed point of view. The progress
of biology demonstrates a variety and suppleness in perception, a marriage between the eye and the mind.[15]

In a stimulating and profound discussion of explanation in biology, Georges
Canguilhem, historian and professor at the Sorbonne, has argued that machines
can only illustrate organisms, not represent them in any proper scientific sense.
Machines are human artifacts executing prescribed geometrical operations. To
regard organisms as machines is to impute human technological qualities to
them, an anthropomorphic view of nature like that of the savage who imagines
a deity behind each everyday occurrence.[16] Canguilhem contrasts the algebraic
constructs employed in the physical sciences with the geometrical, less abstract
formulations of biology. The model in the physical sciences *illustrates* phenomena
of one kind in terms of another, the propagation of sound by reference to the
physics of fluids, for example, while in biology what is sought is a *representation*
of the thing itself, the organism.[17] Without being analyzed into its components,
the biological entity is referred as a whole to some analogous structure with
similar functions. It is the predominant aim of scientific explanation in biology to
represent the whole rather than simply to *illustrate* it by analyzing it into its
parts. The cell theory provided a representation of the whole organism as an

[14] Mendelsohn, "Explanation in Nineteenth-Century Biology" (1965), p. 203.   Errol E.
Harris remarks to similar effect in *The Foundation of Metaphysics in Science* (New York:
Humanities Press, 1965), p. 23. It is worth noting that Schwann was not the uncompromising mechanist that his statement of theory made him out to be. He opposed the
chemists Wöhler, Liebig, and Berzelius in his contention that the yeast produced during fer-
mentation was an organism and not a chemical precipitate, for example.

[15] Agnes Arber, *The Mind and the Eye* (1964).

[16] Canguilhem, *La connaissance de la vie* (1965), pp. 101-127. For a similar discussion in
terms of computers, machines whose function is to convey information, see Michael
Polanyi, "Life Transcending Physics and Chemistry," *Chemical and Engineering News*
(August 21, 1967), pp. 54-66.

[17] Canguilhem, "Analogies and Models in Biological Discovery" (1963).

assembly of essentially similar structural units which always arose from pre-existing cells. This was a scientific representation because it referred to structure and function but it also precisely fulfilled the esthetic requirements of the idea of organic form. In the development of the cell theory we witness the transformation of esthetic presuppositions into scientific knowledge in a manner that parallels Kant's statement that the sense of beauty is an aid to the discovery of truth.

The cell theory may be characterized as an effort to reunite the ideal forms of transcendental morphology with those of scientific observation. The reduction of ideal form to objective knowledge of biological structure is the paradigm—the characteristic guiding system of methods and presuppositions—that makes the progress of biology a coherent sequence from the cell theory to DNA. This process of the objectification of form stands out particularly in Schleiden's discussion of that most beguiling of ideal forms, the spiral.[18] The spiral vessel walls that Nehemiah Grew had drawn and most other microscopists observed became objects of intense speculation among Romantic morphologists. Erasmus Darwin copied one of Grew's illustrations in his *Phytologia* (1800) and considered them to be nutritive absorbent vessels which propelled fluids by waves of contraction in the spiral rings—a kind of "vermicular or peristaltic motion of the vessel, beginning at the lowest part of it, each spiral ring successively contracting itself, till it fills up the tube, must forcibly push forwards its contents without the aid of valves."[19] Here he was indulging his fondness for analogies drawn between plants and animals. He did not observe the contractions, which of course could not occur in rigid plant structures, and simply assumed complacently that they took place.

Goethe published a note on spiral growth in 1831 praising an anatomist who had conjectured that flowers were disposed around the plant stem as a result of "organic rotations." Goethe supposed that a "spiral tendency" might dominate the form of plants; it "actually shapes and determines blossom and fructification." The form of plants was believed to depend upon a constant interplay between the vertical tendency that shapes the axis and the spiral tendency "which predominates in the form of the parts" (*Figure 9*). "In a thousandfold twistings around its center, it performs the miracle that enables a single plant to derive infinite reproductions from within itself." Thus the smallest of the well-known spiral vessels were considered as elementary building blocks—"extremely small parts identical with the whole of which they are a part . . . transmitting their characteristics and tendencies from it in turn. Independent life is attributed to

---

[18] On paradigms in science, see Thomas Kuhn, *The Structure of Scientific Revolutions* (University of Chicago Press, 1962).
[19] Darwin, *Phytologia; or the Philosophy of Agriculture and Gardening . . .* (London: J. Johnson, 1800), p. 17.

them, also the power to move independently and to assume a definite direction."[20] Goethe employed the term "homeomeriae," coined by Greek philosophers for parts identical to the whole, conforming to Anaxagoras' idea that the properties of the whole were identical to those of the parts. For Goethe the whole was the sum of the parts, and no more, and each part displayed the capacities and tendency of the entire organism. Among Goethe's literary effects published after his death was a longer essay in which he recorded additional speculations on the same subject, most notably the claim that spiral vessels

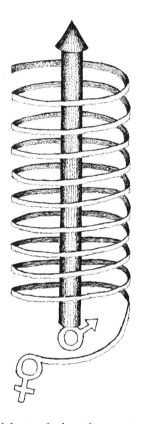

Figure 9. The spiral basis of plant form as imagined by Goethe.

would live on and move for several seconds after being detached from the shoots of certain plants—"not mere mechanical action but the operation of the life principle itself, similar to its operation in animals."

Vallisneria is a plant whose female flowers rise to the surface of ponds or streams until fertilized by floating pollen released from male flowers, whereupon the spiral stem withdraws the flower from the surface and the seeds develop.

[20] "The Spiral Tendency" [1831], in *Goethe's Botanical Writings* (1952), pp. 127-130.

Erasmus Darwin had figured it in *The Loves of the Plants (Figure 10)* and described the floating female:

> Vallisner sits, upturns her tearful eyes,
> Calls her soft lover, and upbraids the skies;

He compared the release of the stamens of the male flowers to the winged males of certain species of insects in which females are flightless and must be sought out by the males. Goethe thought that the males of this flower perfectly displayed the tendency toward the vertical, while the females manifested spiral growth. "Here we see, drawn to our attention by Nature herself, the male and the female, the giver and the receiver together, growing in a vertical and spiral direction."[21]

To Schleiden the lines in the walls of the spiral vessels were not intimations of the ideal but simply the manner in which circulating cell-sap deposited the cell-wall. "The idea involuntarily forces itself upon the mind that the spiral formation is the result of a spiral movement of a fluid on the walls of cells between them and the central jelly. Horkel once actually observed the motion of small globules between the coils of the fiber in progress of formation in *Hydrocharis*." Larger spiral vessels were considered to arise in a similar manner, as a result of the mode of construction of their surfaces. "There is no longer any place for natural-philosophical fantasies about the arrestment of ideal forms of higher types, and such like empty words."[22]

Since spiral construction was not visible in immature cells before the walls had thickened, he concluded that spiral form was a consequence of the manner in which cell walls solidified. The rupture patterns produced in the walls of certain kinds of moistened cells demonstrated the spiral principle of their construction *(Figure 11)*.

In his *Principles of Scientific Botany* (1842) Schleiden gave a more cautious statement, that the origin of spiral structures of cellulose had not yet been observed and that it lay beyond the range of the microscopes then in use. By staining the starch in the transparent walls of growing cells with iodine, he made the spiral structure visible in one of the first uses of the technique of staining, which has since been so greatly developed by histologists. Mechanist and vitalist alike were repeatedly misled by their esthetic presuppositions to suppose that they had seen more than their preparations warranted. But there was an unmistakable trend away from the ideal forms of transcendental morphology toward empirical observations of formative processes within organisms.

Schleiden had a generous opinion of Goethe's contributions and acknowledged that he had greatly clarified problems of development with his notion that flower

---

[21] Based upon David Don, "On the General Presence of Spiral Vessels in the Vegetable Structure . . . ," *Edinburgh New Philosophical Journal,* vol. 6 (1828), pp. 21-23.
[22] Schleiden, "Contributions to Phytogenesis" [1838], p. 245.

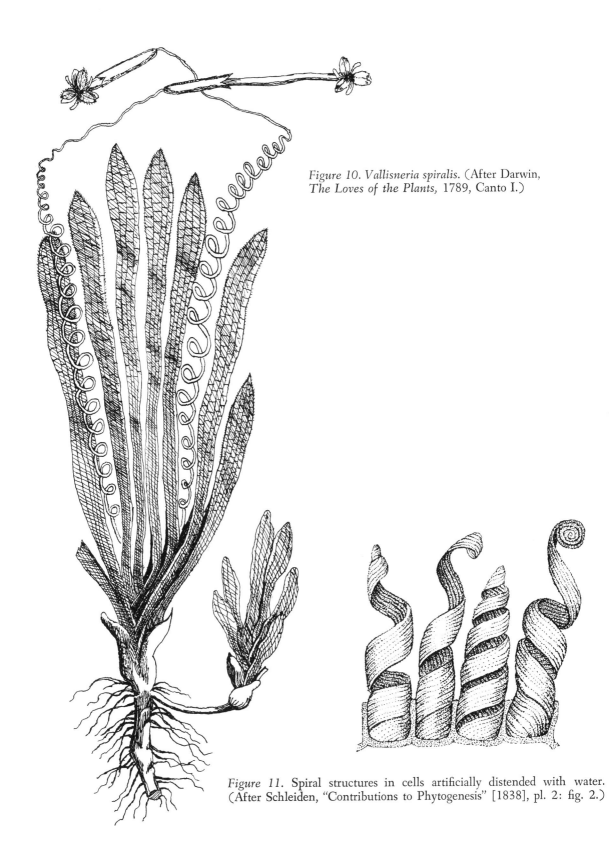

Figure 10. Vallisneria spiralis. (After Darwin, *The Loves of the Plants,* 1789, Canto I.)

Figure 11. Spiral structures in cells artificially distended with water. (After Schleiden, "Contributions to Phytogenesis" [1838], pl. 2: fig. 2.)

parts were foliar (leaf-derived) organs. He stated that Goethe's idea had been slow in gaining acceptance because it was so largely poetic in character. Schleiden could neither recognize nor acknowledge the contribution which esthetic ideas had made to his conception of plant structure. He lamented that in botany "whims of the imagination have taken the place of earnest and acute scientific investigation. In that unbounded region every individual's imagination had naturally equal right; there was a total want of any scientific principle which should undertake the decision between differing opinions of any method." He charged that the *Naturphilosophie* "stirred up together imagination and intellect, musings and thought, poetry and science, into a mixture as distasteful to the true poet as to the clear thinker."

Poetry and science are two regions distinct in their inmost essence, which both lose their whole value when they are intermingled. A poetical treatment of science, and especially of philosophy, the most strict of all sciences, is as repugnant and distasteful to the clearly educated mind, as if one should strike a bargain, order a coat, or call a servant in a poetical speech. A learned poem is empty versified prose—a remnant of the barbarism of the middle ages—poetical science is a troubled mysticism of a cloudy fanatic, of whom, indeed, in the imperfect education of our thinking powers in youth, there will long exist instances."[23]

The sophistication of Schleiden's scientific method stands out in his discussion of the difficulty of properly interpreting microscopic images. Only a few years had elapsed since the invention of achromatic objectives dispelled the halo that surrounded images in compound microscopes as a result of the differential refrangibility of light. He cautioned that gas bubbles in water acquire the appearance of having a very black margin and a pellucid center, that Brownian movement was shown in the dancing movements of all small particles suspended in liquids, and that dust motes were everywhere present. He pilloried Heinrich Friedrich Link (1767-1851), whose microscopic observations had been carried out by an assistant who had prepared the drawings for his publications. Link had contended that his artist's being "totally unacquainted with any of the theories of botany guarantees the correctness of the drawings." Schleiden quite properly insisted that one could see correctly through the microscope only as the result of years of careful observation. Even then, discerning the realities of the structures presented to view was like sensing the character of the landscape on a foggy day. The microscopic observer needed a sophisticated awareness that errors of interpretation constantly arise unless they are guarded against. The highest magnification available in optical systems (limited by the wavelength of

[23] Schleiden, *Scientific Botany* [1842], p. 313. Schleiden refers here to the frontispiece Alexander von Humboldt had drawn for his account of travels in South America, which depicted the god of poetry drawing back a veil to disclose a female figure, signifying nature, and he observes that Goethe seems to have taken it too literally. This drawing was reproduced as the frontispiece in Ritterbush, *Overtures to Biology* (1964).

visible light) is about 2,800 diameters, but only 500 to 1,000 were scientifically available at the time. This improved throughout the century until, by the 1880s, magnifications of 2,400 diameters were frequently claimed. But in 1842, "If any one should assert that he had seen anything magnified 3,000 diameters that could not be seen at a much lower magnifying power, it may safely be pronounced to be mere imagination." In a striking phrase, he says, "The microscope is perfectly innocent of everything of which it is accused."

All microbiologists work in a shadow zone between certainty and surmise. Interpretations are forever being extended beyond the limits of permissible inference only to be called into question by observers whose material or techniques afford a better insight into the phenomena. Most of these interpretations arise from esthetic presuppositions about the character of organic structure and are then subjected to the cruel test of increasingly accurate observation, in the course of which some are admitted to the status of empirical realities. This is the process of the objectification of form. Schleiden was among the first to portray the landscape of organic fine structure, the new realm of form which would become more elaborate from year to year (*Figures 12 and 13*).

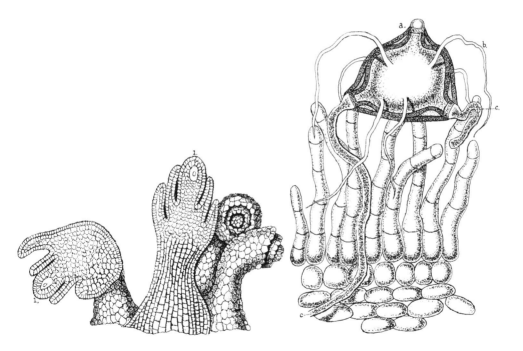

Figure 12. The seed bud of *Passiflora*, showing how cells have formed around the fertilized ovum (*1*). (After Schleiden, *Scientific Botany* [1842], pl. 5: fig. 2.)

Figure 13. A portion of the stigma of *Epilobium*, showing a pollen grain (*a*), with detached fibers (*b*), and two pollen tubes (*c*), whose growth carries gametes to the ovum in the receptacle below. (After Schleiden, *Scientific Botany* [1842], pl. 5: fig. 7.)

One of his finest drawings showed an alga, whose cells revealed surprising degrees of complexity in structure, emblematic of the idea of organic form (*Figure 14*).

Schleiden did not entirely cast aside his natural philosophical inheritance. He wrote that the tree is an inert matrix for a colony of individuals appearing anew each year to cover its surface, an idea that Erasmus Darwin and Lorenz Oken had fondly expounded. He thought, as Goethe had, that the life properties displayed in flowers were more refined than the metabolic processes of the leaves. Just as his drawings reveal a love of natural beauty, his theory of cells was imbued with esthetic considerations. It succeeded in portraying the organism as

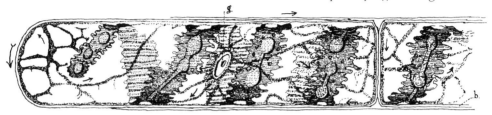

Figure 14. Spirogyrum quinina and the spiral pattern of its components. Arrows show constantly changing streaming movements centered upon the nucleus (*g*). A membrane (*b*) surrounds each cell. (After Schleiden, *Scientific Botany* [1842], pl. 2, fig. 7.)

an entity whose functions depended upon its parts and revealed hierarchical levels of internal complexity. The growth of the whole is mediated by cellular processes in a manner altogether distinct from the addition of layers of molecules to a crystal face. The properties of many-celled organisms could be distinguished from those of any individual cells within their tissues. The criteria of organic form had become applicable to the world of life in a rigorous scientific sense. Nature had been found to mirror art, as Oscar Wilde would later say.

The spiral continued to exert a fascination, perhaps foreshadowing the discovery of the helix of nucleic acids as the matrix of heredity. The spiral habit sometimes found in fibers in the wood of trees has been a persistent subject of speculation. Goethe was delighted at this occurrence and thought it arose from an innate quality. He refused to attribute the twisting of the wood to the merely external influence of winds, and he reported that in dense stands in the forests of Ilmenau between one and two percent of the trees displayed this property.[24] In 1931 and 1932, a hundred years after Goethe's death, a number of articles appeared on the same subject in the pages of *Science* magazine, most of them repeating the supposition that winds cause such twisting, until an article appeared citing statistical evidence that twisting also occurs in the midst

[24] Note to the essay "On the Spiral Tendency in Plants" [1833] in *Goethe's Botanical Writings* (1952), p. 142. Also see Pettigrew, *Design in Nature* (1908), as a conspicuous example of obsession with spirals.

of the forest.[25] If there had been a central computer for scientific information this fact might not have had to be discovered twice, although, if such a computer had been at hand and programmed for this purpose, it would almost certainly have rejected any entry under the name of Goethe—at least if it registered him as a poet and playwright! The American protozoologist Asa Schaeffer discovered that the amoeba travels in a spiral on a cylindrical surface and concluded that all organisms, including man, must move in spirals. He blindfolded a friend, instructed him to walk in a straight line, and plotted his track as a spiral; unfortunately the experiment came to an end when the subject hit a stump (*Figure 15*).

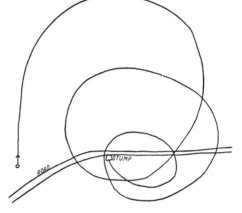

Figure 15. "All moving organisms are within the grip of the spiral urge." (From Schaeffer, *Amoeboid Movement*, 1920, fig. 45, p. 137.)

William Seifriz (1888-1955), a microbiologist at the University of Pennsylvania, whose specialty was the fine structure of protoplasm, reasoned that the spiral form of cotton fibers and other delicate plant structures was evidence that the seemingly formless substance contained within the cell had formative properties that could find expression in the spiral habit of trees. "Spiral development among organisms is the expression of a widespread tendency which is protoplasmic in origin." [26] Thus, as Schleiden had conjectured, the ideal form of the spiral has been traced, perhaps conclusively, to the properties of the cell fluid. Transcendental form yields to the study of fine structure. It is also worth noting that, where biologists have dealt with spheres, spirals, and other forms widespread in nature, there seems to be some danger of being tempted into exaggerated conclusions. The ideal forms of the transcendental morphology continued to carry an esthetic charge, a power to mislead, even after they had been reduced to sober scientific statement.

[25] Glenn Herrick, "Further Notes on Twisted Trees," *Science*, vol. 76 (November 4, 1932), p. 407.

[26] Seifriz, "Twisted Trees and the Spiral Habit," *Science,* vol. 77 (January 13, 1933), p. 51. On another seductive and misleading spiral, the devil's corkscrew, see A. O. Peterson, "Description of new Rodents and Discussion of the Origin of Daimonelix," *Memoirs of the Carnegie Museum,* vol. 2 (1906), pp. 139-191.

Living IV Symmetry

I N THE SAME YEAR as Schleiden's paper on cells in plants there appeared a remarkable publication by one of the most diligent microscopists of the time, a man who had discovered and described great numbers of minute organisms—Christian Gottfried Ehrenberg (1795-1876) of Berlin. Ehrenberg was the first to show that protozoa were abundant in polar waters and the depths of the oceans. He referred to their vast quantities as a "Milky Way" of organisms. Sir James Clark Ross extended these findings to the Antarctic in an expedition in 1839-1843, and Joseph Hooker, the naturalist on the voyage, described the "microscopic herbage." Alexander von Humboldt (1769-1859), whose *Cosmos* was the encyclopedia of science colored by nature philosophy, took these discoveries to demonstrate that life occurs throughout the most hostile regions of the planet.[1] The imagination was thus enabled to conceive of minute organic entities universally diffused through space, a wondrous plenitude of living beings:

> Mysterious ocean where the streams empty,
> Prophetic spirit of materials shifting and flickering around me,
> Living beings, identities now doubtless near us in the air that we know not of.[2]

[1] Humboldt, *Cosmos: A Sketch of a Physical Description of the Universe* (New York: Harper, 1867), vol. I, pp. 341-347.
[2] Walt Whitman, "Starting from Paumanok" (1860), *Leaves of Grass*.

The title of Ehrenberg's monograph was *The Infusoria as Complete Organisms*. He was prompted by belief in an ideal unity of plan to assert that the lower animals were endowed with all of the organs of higher animals. He was among the first to use the achromatic compound microscope, ultimately capable of a resolving power on the order of 0.2μ (1/5000 millimeter, limited only by the wavelength of visible light). In the 1830s magnifications of 1000 diameters or more were achieved, in comparison to 200 diameters, the practical maximum with the simple lens. Thus he was introduced to a whole new world of intracellular complexity, which he misinterpreted entirely. The bodies of protozoa contain inclusions of various kinds just indistinct enough in the microscope to allow scope to the imagination in their interpretation. He thought the liquid vacuoles, which appear and move about within protozoa in the course of nutrition and the exchange of water, were stomachs connected by an intestine. He supposed that protozoa possessed muscular fibers, nerves, fully developed mouths, and a vascular circulation. Ehrenberg's name for them was "stomach animals," and he defined them as animals without spinal cord or heartbeat, with an intestine divided into numerous stomachs, having indefinite form, with both sexes combined in a single organism, and moving through pseudopods (often whirling), without jointed feet[3] (*Figure 16*).

The English anatomist Richard Owen (1804-1892) was an exponent of idealistic morphology. He subscribed to the Oken-Goethe-St. Hilaire theory of the vertebrate skull and also to Ehrenberg's polygastric interpretation of protozoa. Minuteness is relative, he stated, and, thus, there should be no objection to admitting the existence of stomachs in these organisms and "a vascular system . . . throughout their frame." He refused to admit that such complex organisms could be cells. "No mere organic cell . . . has a mouth armed with teeth, or provided with long tentacula."[4] Owen adapted one of Ehrenberg's figures as an illustration to his 1843 lectures on invertebrate anatomy (*Figure 17*). The French microscopist Felix Dujardin (1801-1862) argued decisively against Ehrenberg's interpretation. He maintained that the protozoa were composed of a single characteristic substance that he called "sarcode." The supposed organs of these animals were merely granules or vacuoles in this substance. The amoeba, for example, was composed solely of this glutinous substance, within which numerous granules permitted the observer to ascertain the directions of flow of the sarcode as pseudopods were formed and resorbed into the organism (*Figure 18*).

Foraminifera are predominantly shelled or testate protozoa which form filose or threadlike pseudopods that branch and intercommunicate. Dujardin demonstrated that these structures were naked threads of protoplasm (*Figure 19*).

---

[3] Ehrenberg, *Infusionsthierchen* (1838), p. [xix].
[4] Owen, *Lectures on the Comparative Anatomy and Physiology of the Invertebrate Animals* . . . (London: Longman, Brown, Green, and Longmans, 1843), pp. 25-26.

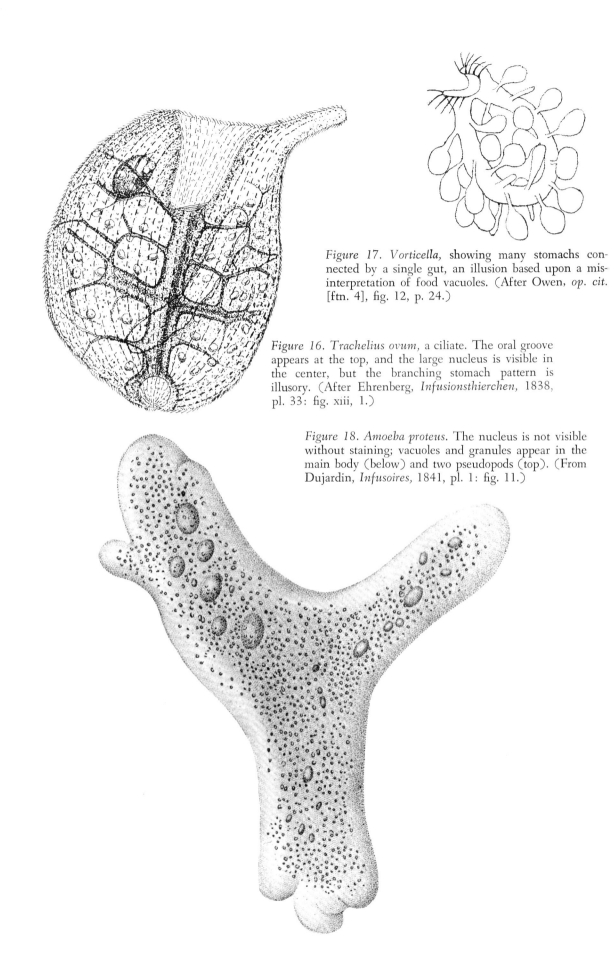

Figure 17. *Vorticella*, showing many stomachs connected by a single gut, an illusion based upon a misinterpretation of food vacuoles. (After Owen, *op. cit.* [ftn. 4], fig. 12, p. 24.)

Figure 16. *Trachelius ovum*, a ciliate. The oral groove appears at the top, and the large nucleus is visible in the center, but the branching stomach pattern is illusory. (After Ehrenberg, *Infusionsthierchen*, 1838, pl. 33: fig. xiii, 1.)

Figure 18. *Amoeba proteus*. The nucleus is not visible without staining; vacuoles and granules appear in the main body (below) and two pseudopods (top). (From Dujardin, *Infusoires*, 1841, pl. 1: fig. 11.)

A number of observers had seen the vacuoles move about, which seemed to rule out their being connected by a single gut, but Ehrenberg stubbornly replied that such motions indicated merely that the interconnections between the stomachs could fold or expand. Dujardin strongly criticized this assertion, arguing that an organ possessing such qualities should be visible because it would have to consist of contractile fibers that could be seen. A very powerful objection, modern in tone and highly significant for the future, was that capillaries in the higher animals approach a limit of fineness around one-hundredth of a millimeter (10μ), which accords with the dimensions of blood corpuscles (the human red blood corpuscle is 7.5μ). "Should one suppose that infusoria 1/10 millimeter in size possess vessels of 1/100,000 millimeter?" This would be inconsistent with limits upon the capillarity of fluids, for there is a size below which capillaries cannot imbibe fluids.[5] Dujardin suggested that the protozoa were

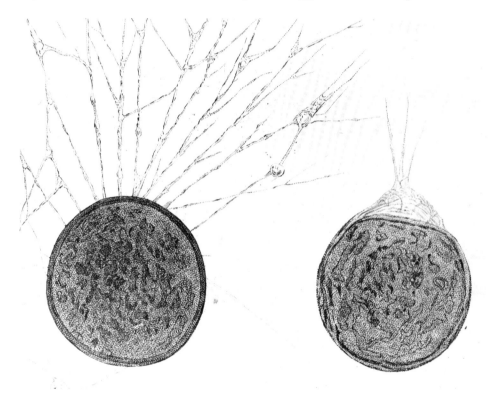

Figure 19. Gromia fluviatilis, a fresh-water foraminiferan, drawn at a magnification of 180 diameters: left, with pseudopods extended; right, commencing to extend pseudopods. (From Dujardin, *Infusoires*, 1841, pl. 2: figs. 1 and 2.)

[5] Dujardin, *Infusoires* (1841), p. 24. Another critic of Ehrenberg was J. Meyen, "Quelques observations sur les organes digestifs des infusoires," *Annales des Sciences naturelles*, 2nd series, zoology, vol. 12 (1839), pp. 122-25.

organized in the manner best adapted to the physical properties of liquid systems of their order of magnitude. This was a very fertile suggestion, implying that the microscopic world would be found to manifest energies, principles of form, and vital phenomena that reflected its scale. A filament of silk, 1/90 millimeter $=11\mu$, appears to be about the same size as the flagellum of a protozoan magnified 320 times, so he supposed that the size of the latter was 1/30,000 millimeter $=1/30\mu$. In dealing with this microscopic new world, especially with animals whose form was constantly changing, one should not expect to apply knowledge of macroscopic processes but seek new principles. The principle that Dujardin sought to apply was symmetry. He noted that in forms possessing cilia these tiny hairlike flagella were arranged in a spiral around the long axis and that many other forms revealed spiral striations or folds. He proposed a rather straightforward system of classification for the infusoria: bacteria, rhizopods, ciliates, and rotifers (which are not protozoa), but termed all of these asymmetrical, evidently believing that bilateral symmetry characterized higher animals only.[6] He erred in supposing that the spiral or helix lacked symmetry, although of course it is not bilaterally symmetrical, and overlooked the conspicuous bilateral and radial symmetry of many forms of protozoa. These errors did not prevent the principles of symmetry from developing as powerful aids to the understanding of the world of microscopic organic forms. Dujardin insisted that the microscopic level must represent a step toward simplicity. This has been one of the most fertile esthetic presuppositions in biology, and symmetry concepts have become one of the principal means of applying it.

Symmetry is a property which figures in almost all serious efforts to explain esthetic responses and often is used as a synonym for harmony or proportion, but it is also susceptible of rigorous mathematical treatment and is in a strict sense a geometric concept. The attractiveness of the circle and sphere to the *Naturphilosophen* probably reflected their rotational symmetry. In being rotated around their centers, they are carried unendingly into themselves. Symmetry is invariance of form during translation or repetition in space. When a bilaterally symmetrical plane figure is rotated 180° around its axis it is carried into itself. A bilaterally symmetrical solid may be analyzed into two mirror images joined at the plane of symmetry (*Figure 20*).

Radial symmetry is manifested in rotation around an axis, either in a plane figure or a solid. In addition to these translations of figure there may be symmetries consisting in invariance of form during repetition, which may be described as unvarying similarity. The scales of a butterfly wing, the elements of a feather,

[6] He listed a few "infusoires symétriques," of which some were gastrotrichs (*ibid.*, pp. 568-570). The idea that higher vertebrates are bilaterally symmetrical and lower animals less so was the leading principle of Bichat's *Traité d'anatomie descriptive* . . . ., vol. 1 (Paris: Gabon et Cie and Brosson, 1801), pp. 4-8.

the vertebrae of a snake all show repetitive symmetry of the kind found in simple ornamental designs. Repetition at equal intervals in time is the musical principle of rhythm that produces the rudiments of a pleasurable esthetic response.[7] Presumably, too, repetitive regularities in natural forms indicate regularity in growth intervals—the principle underlying dating by tree rings, for example. Intuitions of rhythm in nature derive from repetitive similarity in form. Thus the discovery of symmetry in the form of organisms would lead to inferences about regularities in the processes of growth.

Figure 20. Bilateral symmetry manifested in *Flustra gayi* (Savigny), a colonial bryozoan. (From Haeckel, *Kunst-Formen der Natur,* pt. 4, 1900, pl. 33, fig. 16.)

The ideal forms of *Naturphilosophie* partook of symmetry as a transcendental principle. The progress of biology beyond the cell theory has consisted in large measure of demonstrating the existence of significant symmetry properties in the organisms themselves (or in forms abstracted to represent them). The tracing of symmetry conformed to the paradigm of the objectification of form. It consisted in a broadening of the idea of organic form to take into account the differences in the symmetry properties which sometimes exist between organic and inorganic forms. The geometric quality of the concept of symmetry greatly

[7] See Weyl, *Symmetry* (1952), pp. 41-58, and Langer, *Feeling and Form* (1953), pp. 45-54; also Ernst Mach, "On Symmetry" [1871], *Popular Scientific Lectures,* trans. Thomas J. McCormack (Chicago: Open Court, 1895), pp. 89-106.

enhanced the scientific value of visual representations of organisms. At the same
time the manifold usefulness of symmetry principles in the interpretation of
organic form further heightened the esthetic character of biology, greatly increasing the likelihood that visual representations, while scientific, could be referred
to esthetic principles. Thus, biology gained powerful new ways whereby scientific truth could be grasped visually, giving further effect to Kant's assertion
that the sense of beauty is auspicious for knowledge.

One after another, the ideal forms which so delighted the Romantic morphologists would come to be seen as mathematical regularities indicating the
operation of orderly physical or mechanical processes. The most striking instance of the mathematical rationalization of form occurred with the spiral of
the molluscan shell. Descartes had recognized the mathematical properties of
the equiangular spiral, and in 1821 Sir John Leslie, the mathematician, described
it as an "organic" curve and wrote, "This spiral exactly resembles the general
form and elegant septa of the nautilus, which might be adopted with great
effect in many architectural ornaments." [8] The nautilus is a cephalopod mollusc
whose shell had long been celebrated for its beauty. Richard Owen became the
first to describe the organism, in a treatise that attracted widespread attention
(*Figure 21*).

In a communication to the Royal Society in 1838 Canon Henry Moseley, professor of natural philosophy and astronomy in the University of Cambridge,
reported the results of very careful measurements he had made from an illustration of the section of the pearly nautilus (*Figure 22*). He found on radii such
as *klm* or *def* that the width of the outermost whorl was always three times that
of the inner—e.g., *ab* is one third of *bc*—and that "the curve is therefore an
equiangular spiral" or logarithmic spiral. This type of curve has a number of
mathematically interrelated qualities, one being that the figure grows without
changing its shape. No other mathematical plane curve shows this property,
which is manifested in the nautilus even though it grows only in the terminal
region of the shell, unlike a spherical organism which maintains its form by
adding material over its entire surface. The shell of the pearly nautilus displays
even stricter regularity than the curve of its outline, as the sequence of internal
chambers shows a geometrical progression in size. Moseley concluded from this
that the energy available to organisms for their growth is proportional to their
mass, "a value connected by a necessary relation with the economy of the material of each, and with its stability, and the conditions of its buoyancy." [9] He
conjectured that this law of growth might have analogies in other forms of plants

[8] Leslie, *Geometrical Analysis and Geometry of Curve Lines* (Edinburgh: W. & C. Tait,
1821), p. 438.

[9] Moseley, "On the Geometrical Form of Turbinated and Discoid Shells," *Philosophical
Transactions,* vol. 128 (1838), p. 361. Moseley was a versatile mathematician who devised
models for a large number of purely physical processes as well.

Figure 21. *Nautilus pompilius* of the tropical Pacific Ocean in transverse section.
(From Richard Owen, *Memoir on the Pearly Nautilus* (Nautilus Pompilius, *Linn.*)
. . . , London: W. Wood, 1832, pl. 1.)

Figure 22. The logarithmic spiral of the nautilus shell. (After Moseley, *op. cit.*
[fn. 9], pl. 9: fig. 6, p. 351.)

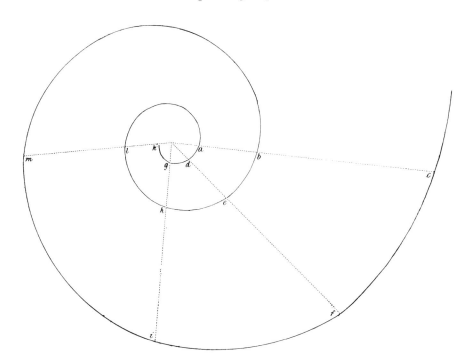

and animals. The way was open for the exploitation of symmetry properties in elucidating the character of submicroscopic growth processes.

John Goodsir (1814-1867), professor of anatomy at Edinburgh, attained distinction as a zoologist, parasitologist, cellular physiologist, and comparative anatomist. He helped to establish the importance of cells in nutrition and secretion and it is a mark of his importance that Rudolph Virchow dedicated his landmark work *Cellular Pathology* to him. Goodsir was much interested in Goethe's morphological writings and also in esthetics, helping to establish a discussion club on the subject in Edinburgh in 1851. One of the papers he read to this group was "On the Natural Principles of Beauty," the same title as the treatise by his friend and colleague D. R. Hay in 1852, who is known also as the author of *Science of Beauty* (1856). Goodsir investigated bone with particular care and sought principles that might relate its microstructure to the shape of major processes. He was fascinated by symmetry concepts and all manifestations of principles of form in animals. His biographer remarks that he possessed "a vein of poesy mingled with a large esthetic feeling that enhanced the beauty of form in his eyes, and rendered more patent the loveliness and adaptation in the mechanism and physiological operations in the varied structure of organisms." [10]

Supposing the logarithmic spiral an emblem of the basic principle of organization in living nature, Goodsir figured it on the cover of the first part of his *Annals of Anatomy and Physiology* (1850) and expressed a hope that Moseley's demonstration of strict geometry in the nautilus might lead to Newtonian laws of organic growth.[11] One side of the obelisk raised to his memory in the Dean Cemetery of Edinburgh bears an incised spiral curve, symbolic of the law of vital force he had hoped to discover and also marking him as a devout adherent of the idea of organic form. The demonstration of the mathematical perfection of the nautilus did not diminish the artistic interest that had so long attached to its shell, but made of it the very embodiment of natural beauty. In the words of one of the most famous of American poems, by Oliver Wendell Holmes, the lowly nautilus progressed from chamber to chamber, leaving its "low-vaulted past" to build "more stately mansions."

> Year after year held the silent toil
>   That spread his lustrous coil;
>   Still, as the spiral grew,
> He left the past year's dwelling for the new,
> Stole with soft step its shining archway through,

[10] Henry Lonsdale, "Biographical Memoir," in *The Anatomical Memoirs of John Goodsir, F.R.S.* (Edinburgh: Adam and Charles Black, 1868), vol. I, pp. 126-27.
[11] Goodsir, "On the Employment of Mathematical Modes of Investigation in the Determination of Organic Forms," *ibid.*, vol. II, pp. 205-219.

Built up its idle door,
Stretched in his last-found home, and knew the old no more.

If Goethe's concept of plant metamorphosis can be deemed to possess any scientific value, it derives from its implicit conception of the stem as a symmetry axis around which the flower parts developed. The use of symmetry concepts to describe the arrangement of leaves in plants (phyllotaxis) dates from 1743. Charles Bonnet (1720-1793) of Geneva, with the help of the mathematician Calandrini, shortly thereafter recognized five modes of leaf arrangement: alternating, opposed, whorls, quincuncial (every fifth leaf appearing in the same vertical plane), or spiral.[12] The spiral sequence of leaf attachments was especially interesting in view of the significance that attached to this figure in Romantic nature philosophy. The botanists K. F. Schimper (in 1835), A. Braun (in 1831 and 1835), and the brothers A. and L. Bravais (in 1837) showed that the spiral lines which could be drawn through leaf attachments showed remarkable properties. Such spirals might be written as fractions, in which the denominator indicates the number of leaves that appear before another leaf is inserted in the same vertical plane as the first, while the numerator describes the number of rotations around the axis before this occurs. The fractions found generally to occur in nature may be arranged in the series 1/2, 1/3, 2/5, 3/8, 5/13, 8/21, 13/34, 21/55, which is the same as that which results from the expansion into a continuous fraction of the irrational number $1/2$ $(\sqrt{5}-1)$. This number is the ratio known as the golden section, which had been considered since Leonardo da Vinci to be intimately connected with all questions of ideal proportion and beauty. The fractions composing the series had been studied by Leonardo Pisano—called "Fibonacci" (1180-1225) and thus called the Fibonacci Series—and also by Johann Kepler (1571-1630). The assemblage of scales in pine cones or the arrangement of the fruits of the pineapple were found to consist of overlapping spirals that conform to this series. The floret and seed arrays of the sunflower manifest 34 short spirals and 55 long ones, thus exemplifying the same symmetry properties (*Figure 23*).

A. H. Church (1865-1937) of Oxford was a botanist who made of the golden section an ideal principle that he correlated with Maxwell's laws of electrical force fields and held to explain plant form (*Figure 24*).

The analysis of plant forms yielding an irrational number was a most unexpected confirmation of the idea of organic form, for, as will be recalled, Haüy's law for crystal form reduced all crystal faces to rational numbers. The almost mystical significance that some writers have since attached to the golden section

---

[12] Bonnet, *Recherches sur l'usage des feuilles dans les plantes* . . . (Göttingen and Leyden: Elie Luzac, 1754), pp. 159-166 and pl. 20 (drawn by Calandrini). On phyllotaxis, see Thompson, *On Growth and Form* (1943), pp. 912-933; Jaeger, *Principle of Symmetry* (1920), pp. 160-170; and Weyl, *Symmetry* (1952), pp. 70-73.

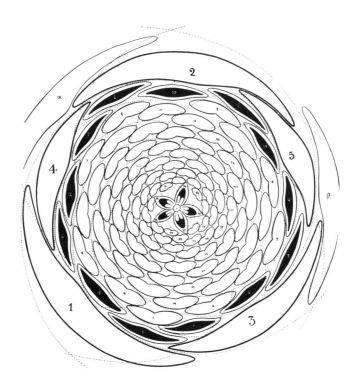

Figure 23. Schematic representation of the spiral construction of the flower of *Helleborus niger,* Christmas Rose; two external bud scales, five sepals, thirteen petals (in black), and stamens arranged in overlapping spirals, eight radiating outward counterclockwise and thirteen, clockwise in this diagram. (From Church, *Types of Floral Mechanism* . . . pt. 1, Oxford: Clarendon Press, 1908, fig. 7, p. 16.)

Figure 24. Transverse section of the apex of a seedling pine, showing overlapping spiral construction, five radiating outward counterclockwise and eight, clockwise in this diagram. (From Church, *On the Interpretation of Phenomena of Phyllotaxis,* "Botanical Memoirs," no. 6, Oxford University Press, 1920, pl. 6.)

derives from the apprehension that it at once expresses the essence of life and of beauty.

If the form of fruit attachments in the pineapple is drawn as a plane surface derived from the cylinder of the entire fruit, the lines of the intersecting spirals will form a parallelogram of meshes to which the individual fruits may be oriented (*Figure 25*).

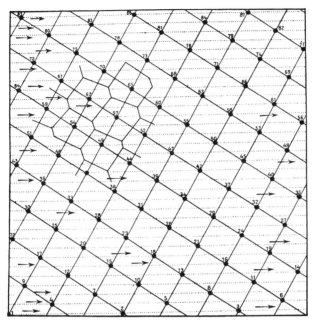

Figure 25. An analysis of fruit arrangement in the pineapple, showing overlapping spirals eight and thirteen in number, while the fruits are numbered from the bottom up on a single spiral curve, known as the "genetic spiral." Note, for example, that the twenty-second stands in virtually the same vertical plane as the first; the genetic spiral makes eight turns around the axis, comprising twenty-one fruits = 8/21, a term of the Fibonacci Series. The approximate shape of the fruits is shown at 49, 54, 57, 62, and 65. (From Jaeger, *Principle of Symmetry*, 1920, fig. 130.)

The Russian investigator G. W. Wulff asserted in 1907 that the distribution of plant organs exactly paralleled the arrangement of molecules in crystals.[13] Such a contention must lead to the introduction of points having irrational coordinates into the space lattice of the crystal and cannot, therefore, be admitted. Moreover, the spiral forms revealed in the arrangement of fruits conform to the logarithmic curve, which cannot be reduced to the simple geometry of the crystalline space lattice. Thus a striking symmetry principle, unique in organic

[13] Wulff, *Snmmetriya N Eya Proyavdenie Vb Prnrodb* (Moscow: 1907). The discovery of crystalline symmetry properties in viruses was further confirmation that the simplest molecular systems display symmetry properties not found in higher organisms. See Helena Curtis, *The Viruses* (New York: Natural History Press, 1965), especially her discussion of the form of bacteriophage and ch. 14, "Art and Architecture," pp. 163-181.

form, became established. The widespread distribution of five-fold radial symmetry in living nature, from the primrose to the starfish, is another example of a symmetry principle unique to organisms, and the recognition of this fact was a further contribution to the objective establishment of the idea of organic form.

A remarkable discovery that further confirmed the existence of peculiar organic symmetry properties took place in 1848 in the laboratory of the young Louis Pasteur (1822-1895). It had been shown by the physicist and chemist Jean Baptiste Biot (1774-1862) that certain crystals had the power of twisting a beam of polarized light, and that certain organic chemical compounds displayed this property even in solution, when they were dispersed into a molecularly diffuse phase in which the crystal lattice ceased to exist. Pasteur discovered that a form of tartaric acid (racemic acid), which was supposed to be optically inactive, was a mixture of equal quantities of two forms of asymmetrical crystals (*Figure 26*). Its optical inactivity was simply a result of the presence of equal

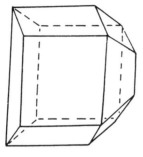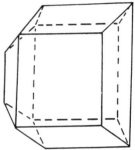

Figure 26. "Mirror image" crystals of tartaric acid (anatiomorphs). The two images cannot be superimposed by translation in space. One crystal is "left-handed" and the other is "right-handed." (From Gardner, *The Ambidextrous Universe*, 1964, fig. 32.)

numbers of "right-handed" and "left-handed" molecules (stereoisomers) of sodium ammonium tartrate. What was astonishing was that the left-handed form of the compound was unknown in living things. When the compound was recrystallized from solution in water, so that the formation of the different forms was left to chance, equal numbers resulted, and the resulting compound was optically inactive. But where the living grape plant synthesized tartaric acid only the dextro-form ("right-handed") was found! Here was further demonstration that symmetry properties at the molecular level distinguished the living from the nonliving. Pasteur overgeneralized somewhat from this experiment and claimed that the production of single optically active substances was the exclusive prerogative of life. He did discover that various moulds grown in optically inactive tartaric acid solutions fermented selectively with one form of molecule, thus causing the solutions to display increasing optical activity. It was this belief which led him in 1854 to suppose that fermenting liquids, inasmuch as they were optically active, must contain an organism and that yeast was thus to be considered an organism, not simply a chemical substance. In 1874 it was established that the asymmetry of organic molecules commonly derives from the capacity of the carbon atom to form asymmetric bonding patterns. The twenty or so amino acids which form all the known proteins are all left-handed, for example, while the sugars in DNA are right-handed. The modern science of stereochemistry, which has made such great contributions to our knowledge of organic fine structure, had its origins in Pasteur's discovery of stereoisomers and the existence of surprising symmetry properties in organisms at the molecular level.[14] Pasteur provided further evidence for the view that organisms manifest special properties of organization by demonstrating the impossibility of spontaneous generation, thus disproving the common notion that nonliving substances periodically gave rise to living forms.

The faculty for perceiving diverse natural forms as variations on a common plan was exemplified strongly by Thomas Henry Huxley (1825-1895), the comparative anatomist whose lucid powers of argument and exposition led him to a great eminence in the English scientific world in the latter half of the nineteenth century. He began his career as a naval surgeon on a voyage to survey the coastal waters of Australia and New Guinea from 1846 to 1850. One of his first papers, sent from South America on the voyage out, dealt with some of the bewildering forms of siphonophores, one of the major groups of jellyfish, or medusae, as they were then called. These lack the more obvious symmetry of the umbrella-shaped scyphozoan jellyfish, which had led Lamarck to denominate the latter group the "Radiata," in which he included the radiate forms of starfish as well. The siphonophores are colonies of individuals radically differing in their form, some being modified polyps (the familiar hydra shape) and others being medusoid (derived from the basic bell shape or umbrella), but extremely diversified into muscular swimming surfaces, bracts, sex organs, or floats (the latter is the familiar blue air sac of the Portuguese man-of-war, *Physalia*). Huxley was the first to visualize these divergent forms as variations on a basic plan. He excitedly wrote his sister from Sydney in 1847 that his elucidation of the nature of *Physalia* "gave rise to several new ideas covering the whole class of animals to which this creature belongs." He had gained an understanding of the entire group, which he conceived to represent a single plan of organization, "one of the great ends of Zoology and Anatomy, viz. the reduction of two or three apparently widely separated and incongruous groups into modifications of the single type, every step of the reasoning being based upon anatomical facts." [15] He proposed grouping all coelenterates into a single major group, "characterized by

[14] Gardner, *The Ambidextrous Universe* (1964), pp. 105-132; Jaeger, *Principle of Symmetry* (1920), pp. 204-283; Vernadsky, "The Fundamental Matter-Energy Difference between the Living and the Inert Natural Bodies of the Biosphere" (1944); Pasteur, "Recherches" (1848).

[15] Letter of August 1, 1847, quoted in Leonard Huxley, *Life and Letters of T. H. Huxley* (1901), vol. I, p. 36.

numerous and striking properties of organization," for which in 1856 he coined
the name Hydrozoa.[16] In 1848 he sent his first important paper to the Royal
Society, in which he described the "foundation membranes"—the two layers of
epithelia, ectoderm and entoderm, the principal body tissues of all coelenterates,
which constitute "a complete identity of structure" among them (*Figure 27*).

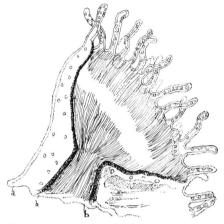

Figure 27. The ectoderm (a) and entoderm
(b) of a scyphozoan jellyfish. (After Huxley,
"On the Anatomy and the Affinities of the
Family of the Medusæ" [1849], in *Scientific
Memoirs,* vol. 1, 1899, pl. 4: fig. 29.)

Huxley had succeeded in applying to all coelenterates the symmetry conditions
conspicuously present only in the simpler forms—a noteworthy example of an
esthetically satisfying conception of a group of organisms. This was an extremely
significant discovery, from which followed Haeckel's gastræa theory and many
other important precepts in comparative anatomy.

It is interesting to note that Huxley arrived at this conclusion in consultation
with William McLeay, author of the speculative classification based on nesting
circles, who lived in Sydney when Huxley stayed there and whose library
Huxley used in preparing his early papers. "I was astonished to find how closely
some of my own conclusions had approached his, obtained many years ago in a perfectly different way. I believe that there is a great law hidden in the 'Circular
system' if one could but get at it."[17] In his first attempt to classify the lower
organisms Huxley arranged them into groups in a circle, which clearly indicates
the influence of idealistic concepts of form. His paper on the medusae won him
great acclaim in England. He was elected a fellow of the Royal Society at the
age of twenty-five on the strength of it and awarded its Royal Medal the next
year. After a delay of several years awaiting a grant for publication expenses, his
important treatise on the medusae was published, with drawings made during
the voyage that demonstrated the full extent of his accomplishment (*Figure 28*).

[16] Huxley, "Ueber die Sexualorgane der Diphydae und Phosphoridae" [1851], *Scientific
Memoirs,* vol. 1 (1889), p. 124. This paper was read to the Linnaean Society in 1849
(Leonard Huxley, *Life,* 1901, vol. I, p. 35).
[17] Letter of October 1849 to Edward Forbes, *Scientific Memoirs,* vol. 1 (1899), p. 34.

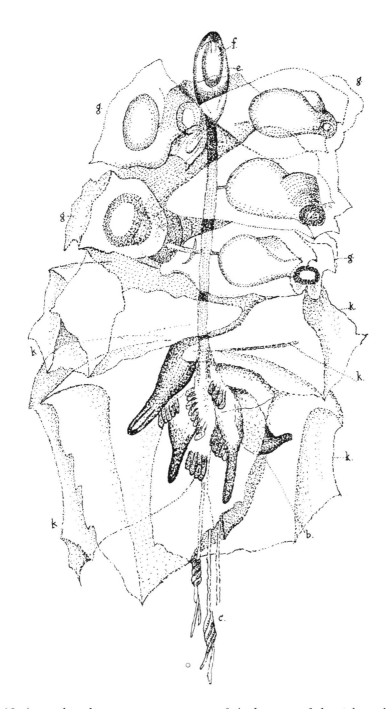

Figure 28. A superb and accurate representation of *Agalma,* one of the siphonophore jelly-fish: *e,* float; *f,* air sac; *g,* swimming organs; *k,* bracts; *k',* gastrovascular canals; *b,* polypite or gastrozooid; *c,* tentacles of *b* with spiral cnidobands. (After Huxley, *The Oceanic Hydro-zoa . . . ,* London: Ray Society, 1859, pl. 7: fig. 1.) The accuracy of the figure may be judged by comparing it to A. G. Mayer, *Some Medusae from the Tortugas* (Museum of Comparative Zoology Bull. No. 37, 1900.)

Huxley conceived of form as a dynamic process of a definite character wherein successive states succeed one another independently of external conditions. The mere "morsel of some protein compound, fresh from the laboratory of the chemist . . . undergoes no change which may not be traced to the immediate and direct operation of some new or varying external condition."[18] A conception of formative processes that aims to distinguish between living and nonliving is an application of the idea of organic form. There are many elements of the idea of organic form in Huxley's scientific work although he maintained rigorous empiricism in his statements about method. As an example of his eloquence and a statement of his positivism, a vivid passage of 1853 may be quoted:

But who seeks absolute truth? Flattering as they were to our vanity, we fear it must be confessed that the days of the high *a priori* road are over. Men of science have given up the attempt to soar eagle-like to some point amidst the clouds, whence the absolute relations of things could be securely viewed; and at present, their more useful, if more ignoble course, may be compared to that of the flocks of sparrows in autumn, which one sees continually halting, yet always advancing—flying from tree to tree, noisily jubilating in each, as if that were assuredly the final nesting-place and secure haven of sparrows, and yet as certainly taking their departure after awhile, in search of new acquisitions. We must build our theories, in these days, as we do our houses: giving up all attempt at Cyclopean architecture, let us bethink ourselves rather of the convenience of our successors, who will assuredly alter, and perhaps pull them down, to suit the needs of their own age; and if we seek their gratitude, let us strive not so much to knit our materials firmly together (which will only give them more trouble and yield us less thanks), as to see that they are separately sound and convertible.[19]

This rhetorical flourish, so characteristic of Huxley, was not a prelude to a penetrating act of discovery but the preface to a long article in which he sought to discredit the cell theory! He seems to have been prompted by an awareness that many of the most important formative processes are subcellular and that the cell theory to date had given no satisfactory account of them. Only in 1850 had Ferdinand Cohn shown the identity of the protoplasm of the plant and animal cell and not until 1860 was it generally realized that protoplasm in animal cells manifested contractile and streaming properties and conducted basic metabolic processes. The movement of granules in amoeba and other protozoa as observed by Max Schultze (1825-1874) and the observations of Anton de Bary (1831-1880) on the slime molds, where naked protoplasm exhibited a surprising capacity for coherent motion, contributed to a realization that this substance was so constituted as to perform many of the functions formerly attributed, rather mysteriously, to the organization of cells. By 1868 Huxley had altered his views and maintained that protoplasm was "the physical basis of life" (*Figure 29*).

[18] Huxley, "The Cell-Theory" [1853], *Scientific Memoirs,* vol. 1 (1899), p. 242.
[19] *Ibid.*, pp. 249-250.

In his writings on comparative anatomy, Huxley betrays an esthetic sensibility, a fondness for the common ideal plan, of which he thought there were only five for the animal kingdom. His criticism of Cuvier, who had sought to explain all animal structures in functional terms of their utility to the organism, is highly reminiscent of Kant's criticism of utility as a basis for the sense of beauty. The beauty of birds, the radial symmetry of the sea urchin, or the diverse elegance of Foraminifera are not of any use to the animals, nor is the harmonious appearance of a few ideal types for all animals. "In travelling from one end to the other of the scale of life, we are taught one lesson, that living nature is not

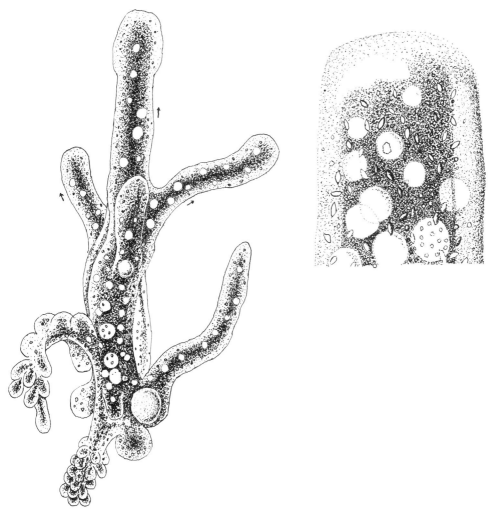

Figure 29. The complexity attributed to protoplasm by the 1870s: left, *Amoeba proteus* with pseudopods and a circular contractile vacuole; right, detail drawn at 500 diameters showing two layers—a clear tip into which darker granular protoplasm advances. (From Leidy, *Rhizopods,* 1879, pl. 1: fig. 3 and pl. 2: fig. 11.)

a mechanism but a poem; not a mere rough engine-house for the due keeping of pleasure and pain machines, but a palace whose foundations, indeed, are laid on the strictest and safest mechanical principles, but whose superstructure is a manifestation of the highest and noblest art."[20]

The influence of esthetic factors on Huxley's conception of life cannot be denied. It is all the more worth taking into account because he was such an eloquent and effective opponent of ideal morphology. He was a stern critic of Richard Owen, against whom he directed a powerful critique of the idea that the skull was composed of vertebrae, the elements of idealistic morphology. He showed numerous differences in development and growth between the skull and the spinal column, pointing out that the notochord was restricted to the latter, the basis cranii was unsegmented, and the processes of the skull differ greatly in number from those of the spinal column.

Those who, like myself, are unable to see the propriety and advantage of intro-ducing into science any ideal conception, which is other than the simplest possible generalized expression of observed facts, and who view with extreme aversion any attempt to introduce the phraseology and mode of thought of an obsolete and scho-lastic realism into biology, will, I think, agree with me, not only in the negative conclusion, that the doctrine of the vertebral composition of the skull is not proven, but in the positive belief that the relation of the skull to the spinal column is quite different from that of one part of the vertebral column to another.[21]

He also criticized Ehrenberg's polygastric notions of protozoan form, which he called "wonderful illustrations of what zoological and physiological reasoning should *not* be."[22]

The towing-net of the *Rattlesnake* had often brought in numbers of simple creatures, which Huxley named *Thalassicola*, derived from the Greek words for sea-jelly. They were radiolaria, single-celled animals attaining a diameter of several millimeters which float in great numbers on the surface of the sea, nearly always with exquisitely formed siliceouus skeletons (which accumulate on the ocean floor after the animals die as "the radiolarian ooze") (*Figure 30*).

Huxley's strong belief that protoplasm was the physical basis of life led him into a surprising interpretation of gelatinous masses apparently dredged up in mud from the bottom of the Atlantic in 1857 by H.M.S. *Cyclops*, which was surveying the route proposed for the Atlantic cable. Within these masses were minute disc-shaped bodies which Huxley at first dismissed as inorganic because

---

[20] Huxley, "On Natural History, as Knowledge, Discipline and Power" [1856], *Scientific Memoirs*, vol. 1 (1899), p. 311.

[21] Huxley, "On the Theory of the Vertebrate Skull" [1858], *Scientific Memoirs*, vol. 1 (1899), pp. 584-585.

[22] Huxley, "Zoological Notes and Observations . . ." [1851], *Scientific Memoirs*, vol. 1 (1899), p. 89.

they dissolved in acid. But in 1861 the English protozoologist G. C. Wallich pointed out that they were identical to minute bodies found in chalk deposits, and shortly thereafter Huxley re-examined his *Cyclops* material with a better microscope and found that the gelatinous substance was itself divided into lumps, leading him to believe that it was a primal organic substance from which the discs might have arisen. Here were "masses of protoplasm . . . deep-sea 'Urschleim,'" a living substrate of naked jelly seemingly capable of generating simple marine organisms. Huxley's belief in its existence arose largely from the organic form of the discs found associated with it. He named the supposed organism *Bathybius Haeckelii* after the German zoologist[23] *(Figure 31)*.

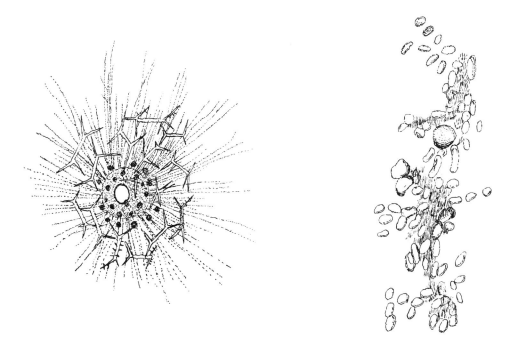

Figure 30. A radiolarian, showing the central capsule (and within it zooanthellae and oil drop), loose spicules, and radiating pseudopods. (After Huxley, "Zoological Notes and Observations Made on Board H.M.S. Rattlesnake During the Years 1846-1850" [1851], *Scientific Memoirs,* vol. 1, 1899, pl. 11: fig. 26.)

Figure 31. Bathybius, supposed to be naked jelly from the sea bottom and thought to be the primal substance of life. (After Huxley, "On Some Organisms Living at Great Depths . . . ," in *Quarterly Journal of Microscopical Science,* vol. 8, 1868, pl. 4: fig. 1a.) The nature of the coccoliths illustrated in other figures of this plate may be readily seen by comparing Huxley's drawings with F. E. Fritsch, *The Structure and Reproduction of the Algae,* vol. 1 (Cambridge University Press, 1935), fig. 169P,S.

[23] Huxley, "On Some Organisms Living at Great Depths in the North Atlantic Ocean" [1868], *Scientific Memoirs,* vol. 3 (1901), p. 337.

Sir Wyville Thomson, leader of the *Challenger* expedition, the greatest marine biological exploration undertaken up to that time, reported to Huxley in 1878 that the substance was not found to occur as predicted and, what was worse, when certain marine specimens were placed in preservative, a dark precipitate formed which was very like the "mud" found in station samples from the *Cyclops*! At the meeting of the British Association in 1879 Huxley made a point of "eating the leek" as he put it and frankly disavowed *Bathybius* as a "very questionable sort of character" that had not lived up to the promise of its youth—"more or less of a black sheep."[24] The discs were coccoliths—calcified secretions of single-celled algae which are common objects in marine deposits. They presented an interesting problem of interpretation, which has many counterparts in twentieth-century studies of microfossils or other minute structures. Huxley had first dismissed them as inorganic in spite of their circular form, although he soon changed his opinion when they were found to resemble constituents of chalk. One of the major applications of the idea of organic form in science is in determining the character of unknown substances, whether or not they are "organized" and, thus, to be considered as products of organic process. A second interesting aspect of the Bathybius episode is how reminiscent it was of Oken's primal mucus. Like the reduction of jellyfish to a single type, the notion of primordial living ooze reveals the influence of Romantic natural philosophy. Esthetic in conception, these ideas could be translated into rigorous scientific concepts: the single plan for coelenterates was given objective demonstration in their foundation membranes and protoplasm was asserted to be the physical basis of life. Huxley considered it a "profound truth, that the study of the structure of living beings originated in the wonder excited by their actions."[25] It seems fitting, therefore, that this great biologist, distinguished by such powers of perception, would have contributed to the first issue of *Nature,* the celebrated weekly journal of science that he helped to found, his own translation of the fragment "On Nature" (1780), the most impassioned lines Goethe wrote on his idea of nature. Huxley describes the genesis of visual representations as "that fashioning by Nature of a picture of herself, in the mind of man, which we call the progress of Science."[26] In his avowal of esthetics, his discovery of basic symmetry in coelenterates, his reflections of transcendental morphology and circular classification, and in his readiness to believe in the *Bathybius* Huxley reveals the historical persistence of these elements in the idea of organic form. He banished the transcendental aspects of the ideal unity of plan from morphology but did as much as any scientist to demonstrate significant common aspects of form. Unquestionably, he owed much of his success to a powerful esthetic sense in the service of a rigorous philosophy of scientific method, in

[24] Leonard Huxley, *Life* (1901), vol. II, p. 6.
[25] Huxley, "The Cell-Theory" [1853], *Scientific Memoirs,* vol. 1 (1899), p. 243.
[26] *Nature,* vol. 1, no. 1 (November 4, 1869), p. 10.

which he stands as a forerunner of the central modern tradition in biology.

Ernst Heinrich Haeckel (1834-1919) is perhaps best known as the leading nineteenth-century exponent of Darwinism in Germany. He was trained as a microbiologist under Rudolf Kölliker in Würzburg and Johannes Müller in Berlin and became professor of zoology at Jena. His first monograph, devoted to the radiolaria, described about one hundred and fifty new species and was accompanied by exquisite drawings. He was greatly influenced by Alexander Braun, whose work on the symmetry of leaf arrangements was mentioned above, and also by the *Naturphilosophie,* toward which Müller was inclined. He went so far as to give Goethe equal credit with Charles Darwin as the co-originator of the theory of evolution! The influence of Goethe shows in the title of his first theoretical treatise, *General Morphology,* and its subtitle, *The Science of Organic Form.* Here he portrays the course of evolution as the result of a dialectical interplay between internal and external formative forces (*Bildungstriebe*). In this work Haeckel propounds the doctrine of "general promorphology or universal theory of basic forms of organisms."

Haeckel's morphology consists of the application of symmetry principles to the task of classifying all organic forms. The three primary groups are (1) "Lipostaura," lacking cross axes or a single median plane and including sponges and the spherical forms of radiolaria and pollen grains; (2) "Stauraxia," radially symmetrical forms of which the more regular were subdivided according to the ideal platonic solids, a group including most lower invertebrates; and (3) "Zeugita" or "Allopola," bilaterally symmetrical forms with a median axis of symmetry, including higher animals. While there are internal confusions in this grouping, it succeeded in showing that symmetry principles were widely applicable to the classification of animals and the analysis of their forms.[27] This classification had the virtue of separating radiolaria and heliozoa, with spherical symmetry, from echinoderms and most coelenterates, with radial symmetry around an axis, and these in turn from the ctenophores and most anthozoan coelenterates.[28] But his system is especially noteworthy as a manifestation of Haeckel's belief that the symmetry principles of organisms closely approached those of crystal structures (*Figure* 32).

Haeckel believed that the internal structure of organisms could be deduced from the regularities of their external form, for these were manifestations of equilibrium relations at the molecular level. He thought it should be the aim

[27] A. P. de Candolle, *Théorie élémentaire de la botanique* . . . (Paris: Déterville, 1813), pp. 90-154, constitutes an early but far less precise attempt to employ symmetry principles as characters in the establishment of major plant groups, as Cuvier had also attempted to do. It would be interesting to trace the earlier history of the role of symmetry properties in systematic biology.

[28] Haeckel's categories show a general resemblance to those stated by so outstanding an authority as Libbie H. Hyman, *The Invertebrates: Protozoa through Ctenophora* (New York: McGraw-Hill, 1940), pp. 18-21 and fig. 4.

of the science of morphology to infer from the shapes of organisms the characteristics of the three-dimensional space-lattice that would best account for their
internal properties and fine structure. "This secure promorphological foundation
makes possible a mathematical understanding for organic individuals just as in
crystals."[29] Haeckel here betrays the esthetic presuppositions that guided his
interpretation of the fine structure of microscopic marine organisms. The radiolaria he drew for his 1862 monograph and its second edition in 1887 are exquisite
in structure and astonishingly regular in outline. Compared to Huxley's sketch
(above, *Figure 30*, p. 61), they are wonders of symmetry and design. Under
the influence of his aspirations to discover strict symmetry, Haeckel altered his
drawings to conform to his belief in the geometrical character of organic form.
A process of generalizing abstraction resulted in representations that were im-
provements upon nature. The observer who inspects a radiolarian under the
microscope today will be disappointed at his impressions of reality as compared
to the crisp and symmetrical outlines of Haeckel's superb lithographs. Many of
his drawings depicted features in the fine structure of organisms that exemplified
his tendency to perceive regularities that might be interpreted as positive evidence
for an ultramicroscopic space-lattice (*Figure* 33).

As these drawings refer the organism to a scientific concept of structure in space,
they conform to the idea of representation proposed earlier. They cannot be
dismissed as illustrations on grounds that they refer their objects to some extra-
scientific principle, yet just as clearly they result from the influence of esthetic
presuppositions that the world of microscopic nature will display distinctive
regularity. Haeckel was an accomplished watercolorist and keenly interested in
art. The radiolaria are among the most exquisite objects in nature, more likely
than most other organisms to excite his imagination and to mislead his eye. The
beauty of Haeckel's radiolaria was projected from his own imagination. Thus,
his drawings take on a standing as works of art that by his time was no longer
attributed to literal representations. D'Arcy Wentworth Thompson came to
believe that some of the radiolaria drawn by Haeckel were utter fabrications.

Haeckel wrote that the generation of form by protoplasm deserved to be
compared to the creation of works of art by man. The lower organisms seemed
to evince a common purposiveness that was the basis of their beauty and
accounted for their effects on human feeling. To Haeckel this seemed adequate
ground for attributing a soul to protoplasm! These thoughts prompted him to
issue a splendid series of one hundred lithographs between 1899 and 1904 under
the title *Art Forms of Nature*, showing plants, insects, molluscs, and vertebrates,
but consisting mostly of his beloved protozoa and coelenterates (46 of the lithographs are devoted to these two groups). He appended a table of basic forms

---

[29] Haeckel, *Generelle Morphologie* (1866), vol. I, p. 543. For his popular exposition of
this view, see *The Wonders of Life* (1905), pp. 170-209.

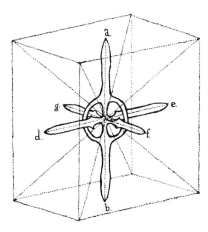

Figure 32. Axes of symmetry, *ab, de, fg,* in a radiolarian (*Actinomina drymodes*), which define a rectangular solid. (From Haeckel, *Generelle Morphologie,* 1866, vol. I, pl. 2: fig. 20.)

Figure 33. The spumelline radiolarian *Actinomma drymodes* (diameter 0.15 mm.) in a drawing that represents illusory structures and an exaggerated degree of regularity. (From Haeckel, *Die Radiolarien,* 1862, pl. 24: fig. 9.)

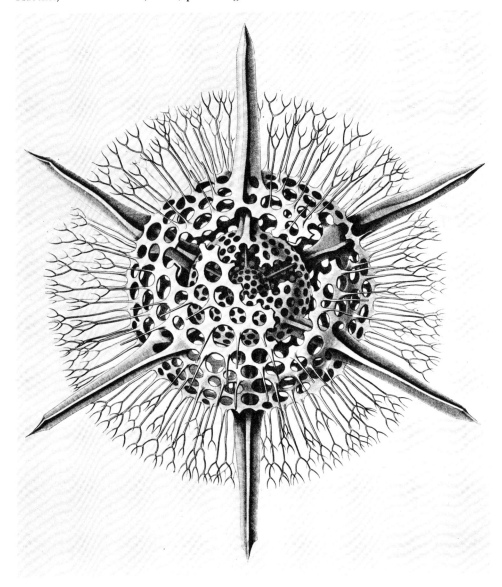

like those of his *Generelle Morphologie* of 1866, so that the reader could perceive the symmetry properties of the organisms represented.[30] To make one's way through this profusion of natural forms is a remarkable experience. There can be no clearer indication of the esthetic potential latent within the accumulation of images with which biology had enriched human experience in the course of the previous one hundred years. They call to mind the superb *Vélins du Muséum National d'Histoire Naturelle* in Paris, wherein a succession of painters to the French court since the seventeenth century portrayed flowers and animals, but here the emphasis is on the microscopic world with an uncompromising insistence on abstract beauty and symmetry. *The Kunst-Formen der Natur* is one of the first indications that the forms introduced to science by morphology and microscopy in the nineteenth century might have a broader esthetic appeal.

Haeckel was thrilled by the seeming discovery of the *Bathybius,* "that the sea floor of the open oceans in the more important depths (beyond 5,000 feet) is covered with enormous masses of free living protoplasm." He secured some deep sea mud dredged from a depth of 2,435 fathoms in 1869 and found a substance in it that showed all the reactions then commonly regarded as diagnostic for protoplasm. He supposed that it represented a primordial stratum of life coming into existence on the ocean floor, growing like crystals from a solution.[31] He had made a special study of the "monera," as he called them, organisms conceived to be naked protoplasm, and he included *Bathybius* in this group.[32] Haeckel was drawn to the simpler forms of life in hopes of finding manifestations of crystal structure. Shortly before his death he published a speculative work on souls in crystals, which he thought to govern their three-dimensional parallel arrangements of molecules in a manner almost identical to the forces governing the composition of the monera.[33] This concept was antithetical to the idea of organic form in that it identified crystalline order with that of living systems. Haeckel's misinterpretation of radiolaria is an important demonstration that in certain contexts the idea of organic form could help the investigator resist the temptation to simplify representations of living form. Another example of illusory regularity, conceived in contradiction to the idea of organic form, was the geometrical space-lattice of protoplasm.

Otto Bütschli (1848-1920), professor of zoology at Heidelberg, was a leading microbiologist with noteworthy achievements in the investigation of single-celled algae, the process of cell-division in animals, and bacteriology. He made a bold

[30] Haeckel, *Kunst-Formen der Natur,* Supplement (1904), p. 49. He hoped that this work would communicate the beauty of scientific knowledge to the lay public, anticipating Michael Polanyi's comment, "All true appreciation of science by the public continues to depend on the appreciation of such beauty. . . ." (*Personal Knowledge* [1958], p. 172).

[31] Haeckel, *Studien über Moneren* (1870), pp. 86-106 and 177-182.

[32] Haeckel, "Monograph of Monera" (1869).

[33] Haeckel, *Kristallseelen* (1917), p. 149.

attempt to solve the problem of organic form by postulating a space-lattice in protoplasm along whose lamellae the force of surface tension might account for the observed motions of such single-celled animals as the amoeba. He devised artificial foams by making emulsions of certain salts and olive oil, in which he could readily observe a network structure *(Figure 34).*

He then devised experiments in which the model drops of foam displayed streaming phenomena such as those of the amoeba *(Figure 35).*

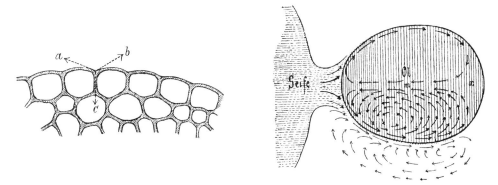

Figure 34. The foam structure postulated by Bütschli for protoplasm, showing how surface tension in the uppermost layer may produce a flat surface while causing internal alveoli to draw together. (From *Mikroskopische Schäume,* 1892, fig. 3, p. 24.)

Figure 35. A drop of oil foam (*öl*) brought into contact with soap (*seife*), left, that lowers the surface tension of the drop and causes streaming movements; m = middle stream moving forward and x = resting zone. (From Bütschli, *Mikroskopische Schäume,* 1892, fig. 9, p. 43.)

He was able to induce streaming phenomena lasting for a week at a time in his emulsion drops and cause more rapid movements with heat and electricity, rather as could be done with living amoebae. "The depiction of foam drops is only the beginning of my attempt: that is the imitation and eventual explanation of the structure of protoplasm. While proceeding toward this I must emphasize the really astonishing similarity which foam drops show to protoplasm if they have been properly formed . . . ."[34]

When Bütschli investigated the structure of protoplasm in preparations of organic tissues in various fixatives, he found a honey-comb structure that he hailed as confirmation of his belief that surface tension acting along lamellae would account for the phenomena of amoeboid movement. The size of the meshes he postulated for the network was just within the range of the optical microscope, between 0.5μ and 1.0μ, and he published numerous drawings of the supposed structure in protozoa and their pseudopods, and also in bacteria[35] *(Figure 36).*

[34] Bütschli, *Mikroskopische Untersuchungen* (1892), p. 58.
[35] Bütschli, *Bau der Bakterien* (1890), pls. 3-5.

Bütschi acknowledged that the surface-tension effects that he thought he observed did not perfectly correspond to the phenomena he observed in living amoebae (in fact, he had to invent a very thin membrane within which protoplasm was conceived to flow in opposing directions in order to account for the appearance of an amoeba that inexplicably failed to generate streaming currents in the surrounding water).[36] Nonetheless he was so pleased to have found a structure like that whose existence he had imagined that he ignored such difficulties and reported that he had solved the problem of amoeboid movement.[37]

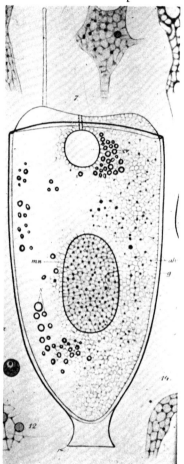

Figure 36. The illusory foam structure of protoplasm in a sessile ciliate, *Scyphidia.* Such structure only occasionally exists in the sense Bütschli supposed and only in a few specialized parts of protozoa. (From Bütschli, *Mikroskopische Schäume,* 1892, pl. 2: fig. 7.)

[36] Bütschli, *Mikroskopische Untersuchungen* (1892), p. 220.
[37] This has remained a problem for lively scientific controversy; see, e.g., P.P.H. deBruyn, "Theories of Amoeboid Movement," *The Quarterly Review of Biology,* vol. 22 (1947), pp. 1-24.

Bütschli was one of the first to seek to apply ideas from the physics of fluids and colloid chemistry to the fine structure of protoplasm, which was an outstanding contribution to biology, highly germane to the problem of organic form, and one that should win Bütschli a more prominent place than he has been assigned heretofore in the history of science. But the web structure he observed in protoplasm, except for a few specialized organs, were generally by-products artificially produced by the fixatives he employed in preparing his specimens.[38] He had started from esthetic presuppositions in favor of a three-dimensional space lattice with specified symmetry properties. The structure he repeatedly found when he directed his microscope at organic tissues was an illusion induced by his expectations.

Bütschli is only one example of a brilliant school of microbiologists, students of Hertwig and von Sachs, that flourished in Germany toward the end of the nineteenth century and continued into the 1930s. When the history of their accomplishments comes to be written, prominence undoubtedly will be given to the visual character of their genius. Richard Goldschmidt, the geneticist whose first employment was as Bütschli's assistant, has written as follows:

When I mention Bütschli's draftsmanship it comes to my mind how many of the old zoologists had this gift. I have already discussed Haeckel; I could add Carl Chun, the great marine zoologist, who adorned his house with frescoes; Boveri, who did oil paintings of merit; Doflein, the protozoologist, who was good at water colors; and many others. This ability can be understood as part of the sense of form which makes a good naturalist and morphologist, and even today, when scientific illustration has become less important, many examples of the gift of draftsmanship will be found among zoologists. With Bütschli this was only a part of an all-around artistic nature which was revealed only to his friends. It was said that in his younger years he had a beautiful singing voice, which he had ruined by chain-smoking cigars. When I knew him he still occasionally played the piano. In his spare time and during vacations he was a voracious reader of belles-lettres, and he was well acquainted with literature in many languages. Once he confided in me that he was occupied in translating Shakespeare's *Tempest*, one of his favorites, into German verse. The ease with which he produced rhymed skits for occasions in the laboratory suggests that he may have indulged secretly in verse writing.[39]

Lest these examples convey the impression that such erroneous interpretations arise simply from an unscientific indulgence in esthetics, I will briefly mention the work of Theodor Boveri (1862-1915), one of the most brilliant microbiologists in history, the virtual founder of the science of cytogenetics. He was also conspicuous for his sensuous, artistic character. Scientific drawing was a delight

[38] W. B. Hardy, "The Structure Produced in a Cell by Fixative and Post-mortem Change . . . ," *Journal of Physiology,* vol. 24 (1899), pp. 158-210 and pl. 3: figs. 18-19.
[39] Goldschmidt, *Portraits from Memory* (1956), p. 63.

for him. Just as Julius von Sachs, the botanist, is frequently quoted as saying, Boveri believed that what had not been drawn had not been seen: "For Boveri the microscopic *picture* is the point of departure, that is to say, a visible condition or process, and not an abstract idea."[40] He frequently observed that he would have liked to have become a painter. One of his best paintings, a Bavarian landscape of 1908 in oils, shows a proficiency with tone and subtlety of composition that mark it as an accomplished work.[41] He greatly admired the masters of German drawing and Italian art of the fourteenth and fifteenth centuries and records, for example, that the Medici tomb in Florence "completely overpowered" him.

E. B. Wilson, the great American cytologist who also studied with Boveri and who dedicated to him his book *The Cell in Development and Heredity,* said of his work that "it is distinguished by a fine quality of constructive imagination, by a sureness of grasp and an elegance of demonstration, that make it almost as much a work of art as of science."[42] Mechanistic biologists were then claiming that heredity should be investigated as a chemical process unaffected by considerations of the form or structure of the genetic material. Boveri was struck by the symmetrical disposition of the chromosomes in the nuclei in successive cell divisions. This was visually manifested invariance *(Figure 37).* The persistence of the chromosomes, inferred from their symmetry properties, led Boveri to conclude that heredity was controlled by *organized* structures, "units in their manifestations of living processes [which] defy interpretation through physico-chemical processes."[43] Without Boveri's penetrating vision, the significance of the structure of chromosomes might very well have been passed over

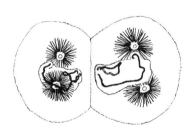

Figure 37. The egg of *Ascaris* in two-celled stage showing the symmetrically corresponding disposition of the chromosomes. (After Boveri, "Die Blastomerekerne von Ascaris Megalocephala und die Theorie der Chromosomindividualität," *Archiv für Zellforschung,* vol. 3, 1909, fig. 24, p. 91.)

[40] Baltzer, *Theodor Boveri* [1962], p. 24.

[41] It is reproduced as a color plate in Fritz Baltzer, *Theodor Boveri . . . ,* "Grosse Naturforscher," vol. 25 (Stuttgart: Wissenschaftliche Verlagsgesellschaft M.B.H., 1962), fig. 8, facing p. 64.

[42] In W. C. Röntgen, ed., *Erinnerungen an Theodor Boveri* (Tübingen: J. C. Mohr, 1918), p. 67. See also Baltzer's discussion of the intuitive and imaginative procedures in Boveri's dispermy experiment, which proved the differential value of chromosomes in heredity, *Theodor Boveri* [1962], pp. 85-92.

[43] Boveri, "Zellstudien II: Die Befruchtung und Teilung des Eies von Ascaris megalocephala," *Jena Zeitschrift für Naturwissenschaft,* vol. 22 (1888), p. 692.

in favor of distracting and premature chemical investigations. He was confident
that morphological analysis would ultimately refine the material of heredity into
definable chemical components, but he recognized that the chemistry of his time
was not equal to the attempt.

Hans Driesch (1867-1941), a student of Haeckel and a philosophically inclined biologist, believed he found evidence for a formative principle overriding
the specialized roles assumed by different cells in the process of embryonic
development. After observing successful development from only a quarter of
the sea-urchin embryo, Driesch concluded that any part of the organism, no
matter how small, retained a "harmonic equipotency" to recreate the whole.
Here again an exaggerated notion of the organizing power of substance attributes
to any part the capacity to regenerate the whole. Boveri discovered that pigments
localized in the developing embryo permitted him to infer that each cell in the
four-cell stage of development had equal portions of material destined to develop
into the major organ systems of the larva. But the next division distributed these
materials unequally, and the cells destined to develop into the body wall never
reached the larva stage if separated from the embryo (*Figure 38*). This proof
that the development of certain cells would be arrested by their separation from
the organism after their primary specialization disproved Driesch's assertions
about "equipotency" and restored a proper understanding of the principles of
emergent order in organic form, which was based upon the more fruitful concept that the capacity for organization changed during the organism's development. Boveri's beautifully executed plates exemplify his care in approaching
questions of development, as opposed to Driesch's equally revealing clumsy
renderings (*Figure 39*).

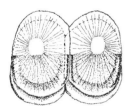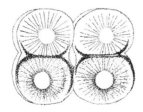

Figure 38. The four-celled stage in the development of the sea-urchin egg shows a sharing
of pigment among all cells, whereas by the eight-celled stage the pigment ring is almost
entirely segregated into the lower four cells. Boveri showed that only the latter retain a
capacity for independent development. (After "Die Polarität von Oocyte, Ei und Larve
des Strongylocentrotus lividus," *Zoologische Jahrbuch, Abteilung für Anatomie und Onto-
genie der Thiere,* vol. 14, 1901, pl. 49: figs. 16 and 17.)

Figure 39. The four- and eight-celled stages in the development of the sea-urchin egg.
(After Driesch, "Entwicklungsmechanische Studien . . . ," pts. III-VI, *Zeitschrift für
Wissenschaftliche Zoologie,* vol. 55, 1893, pl. 1: figs. 15 and 16.)

Driesch's vitalism consisted in a "surrender to an idea."[44] Boveri's esthetic sense, his alertness to symmetry, and what Baltzer calls his "commitment toward organic form" contributed greatly to his remarkable discoveries, so central to modern genetics. "Driesch," he wrote to Spemann in 1902, "has looked somewhat superciliously through his microscope."[45] Boveri's penetrating discoveries arose directly from his vivid sense of "the elementary sculptural laws of organisms . . . . Once we experience the impact of the whole, we sense as it were an intimation from the fathomless depths of primeval matter."[46] The symmetry principles that guided nineteenth-century investigators, their sense of the objective presence of beauty in organisms, are here carried into the modern tradition of cytogenetics, the foundation and point of origin for the scientific understanding of organic form in the twentieth century.

[44] Driesch, *Lebenserrinerungen* (Munich and Basel: Ernst Reinhardt, 1951), p. 304.
[45] Quoted in Baltzer, *Theodore Boveri* [1962], p. 112.
[46] Boveri, *Die Organismen als historische Wesen: Festrede* (Würzburg: H. Stütz, 1906), pp. 30 and 33.

The Progress of V Biological Forms

IN 1907 THE ACA-
démie des Sciences in Paris refused to enter in its index of current research
reports a book entitled *The Physico-Chemical Theory of Life and Spontaneous
Generation*. Stéphane Leduc (b. 1853), the author, who was professor of medicine at Nantes, started from the seemingly unexceptionable premise that the
essential character of a living being was revealed in its form, which biology
seeks to elucidate through investigating the properties of fluids and colloids.
Organisms manifest forms which differ from those of crystals both in general
shape and symmetry properties. Leduc conjectured that the paths of diffusion
followed by drops in solutions might indicate the operation of fields of force
in organisms that would indicate the capacity for order in a two-phase liquid
system. This was an unlikely supposition but not radically dissimilar to proposals
that had been advanced in experimental embryology. Leduc found that various
chemical reactions on a layer of gelatine would produce symmetrical diffusion
patterns (as long as the drops of reagent were symmetrically placed). He excitedly claimed that such experiments "show us the possibility, hitherto unsus-
pected, that a vast number of the forms and colors of nature may be the result
of diffusion. Thus many of the phenomena of life, hitherto so mysterious, present themselves as merely the consequences of the diffusion of one liquid into
another."[1]

[1] Leduc, *The Mechanism of Life* (1914), p. 61.

As Bütschli had done, Leduc tried to manufacture a polyhedral network of cells, but rather than make emulsions whose fine structure might be postulated to be equivalent to that of protoplasm, he simply introduced drops at set intervals and found that polygons were produced in the gelatine substrate. "These tissues of artificial cells demonstrate the fact that inorganic matter is able to organize itself into forms and structures analogous to those of living organisms under the action of the simple physical forces of osmotic pressure and diffusion."[2] R. Liesegang of Düsseldorf made a specialty of studying patterns of diffusion in colloids; these show a striking periodicity, reminiscent of tree rings, and are now known as Liesegang rings. Leduc compared them to the diffusion gratings that produce structural colors in iridescent insect wings and mother of pearl. Here was a rhythmic growth phenomenon that bore a close analogy to formative processes in organisms.

Leduc's attempts to manufacture organic forms are remarkably interesting. He had no basis for supposing that living things grew in the manner of his experiments. Unmistakably, he was prompted by a desire to create organic forms, even though he could maintain the level of symmetry in his preparations only by plotting the points where he would inject drops of reagent. Like Goethe's ideal leaf forms, these preparations cannot be acknowledged to be representations in any scientific sense, and the academicians were justified by this standard in excluding them from the *Comptes Rendus*. They were attempts to reproduce the formal properties of organic beings by systematically altering the composition of solutions wherein crystals were being deposited. They were illustrations, not representations of living beings. Leduc thought they pointed the way toward explaining morphological phenomena, so they must be acknowledged to be scientific conjectures, but their primary significance is betrayed by his frequent exclamations upon their beauty. Leduc's delight in his artificial growths was based upon their formal properties, their esthetic connotations, their embodiment of the idea of organic form in its esthetic sense. The foam theory of Bütschli, while influenced by esthetic presuppositions about the regularity of lamellae in a space-lattice within protoplasm and marred by his emotional refusal to credit contradictory observations, was uncompromisingly a work of science. By comparison, the "plasmagenic" theory of Leduc is an esthetic proposition and his organic forms are works of art (*Figure 40*).

Leduc's emulsions are indistinguishable from some of the "Rayograms" produced by the early abstract photographers Man Ray (b. 1890) and Ladislaus Moholy-Nagy (1895-1946), and to some extent the same processes were employed.[3] Gyorgy Kepes (b. 1906) is well known for his attempts to reproduce

[2] *Ibid.*, p. 66.
[3] Ray, "On Photography," *Commercial Art*, vol. 17 (1934), pp. 62-64; Moholy-Nagy, *60 Fotos: Herausgegebenen von Franz Roh* (Berlin: Klinkhardt & Biermann, 1930); Ray, *Photographs, Paris 1920-34* (Hartford: James Thrall Soby, 1934).

organic form by manipulating the emulsion of photographic plates.[4] Prochnow's *Formenkunst der Natur* (1934) includes a number of plates of the organization that appears in dried lacquer and gelatine, and there is growing interest in such works today.[5] These are not photographs of objects but images produced as a result of structures created in plates of emulsion, projective sculpture, as it were. It would be perverse to insist that Stéphane Leduc was the first to create an

Figure 40. "Osmotic vegetation," the precipitate from a solution believed to "imitate the forms of animated nature without the intervention of any living organism." (After Stéphane Leduc, *The Mechanism of Life*, 1914, fig. 62, p. 163; quoted from pp. 152-3.)

[4] Kepes, *Arts & Architecture* (August 1946), pp. 24-25.
[5] See, e.g., Len Gittleman and Grant Haist, in Frederick P. Walkey, *Photography U.S.A.* (Lincoln, Mass.: DeCordova Museum, December 10, 1967–January 28, 1968).

entirely abstract work of art. But it would be equally difficult to deny that his near-organic constructions are indeed works of art.

As a result of a century-long tendency to incorporate esthetic principles in the interpretation of organic forms, especially to conceive a maximum role for symmetry properties, the external forms of organisms had gained greatly in esthetic value. Nowhere was this more true than at the microscopic level, where emergent order induces the most direct expression of formative principles. In the art of the twentieth century there are innumerable examples of exquisite sensitivity to the inner formative properties of organisms and these stand in direct historical continuity with the efforts of biologists over the previous century to describe the processes by which forms arose. Organic forms appear in painting and sculpture not as illustrations of this or that scientific fact, but as representations of the process of artistic creation itself. The biological motifs in their compositions testify to the artists' awareness of the distinctiveness of the organic form and its superior expressive quality, reflecting an esthetic endowment built up over a century of aspiration toward knowledge of the true nature of life.

Perhaps the first paintings to suggest the expressive qualities of organic forms were those of Odilon Redon (1840-1916), celebrated for his art of fantasy, but the artist who established their importance was Paul Klee (1879-1940). In a 1915 diary entry he described the process of abstraction as the shaping of impure crystals from the fragments of experience: "ich Krystall" [I a crystal] he wrote, in large letters that stand out prominently from the page. Throughout Klee's writings there is an emphasis on spatial properties whose mastery he conceived to be the basis of artistic expression. The regularities of a crystal lattice as a means for analyzing space must have been especially apparent to him because of his deeply musical nature. Many of his compositions conspicuously show a harmonious lattice of verticals and horizontals, but the strict geometry of musical notation has been transformed as though by the experience of music itself. A higher expressive order emerges from the strictly disposed elements. Imposing upon his art the strictest discipline of means, Klee sought an essential basis for expression that he might apply in progressively more complex undertakings. Early in his career he wrote that he felt pregnant with things needing form, that there was a world hidden within him that would be expressed if he could devise appropriate means of doing so. His works prompt the viewer to conceive an organic framework, an irregular space frame wherein strict order is rhythmically displaced. Thus, the work of art gains the power to reshape our experience by imposing demands upon our mode of perceiving it.

Klee's radical effort to invent new ways of depicting nature was greatly influenced by his understanding of, and delight in, organic form. In 1902, during his Italian tour, he found the aquarium at Naples "extremely stimulating" and the octopi "especially expressive." "A gelatinous, angelic little creature (transparent and spiritual) swam on its back with incessant movement, swirling a delicate pennon."[6] He recognized that a close knowledge of natural form would contribute greatly to the development of his art and in 1902 he enrolled in a course of anatomy in hopes of gaining a thorough mastery of the subject. In his long walks he keenly observed flowers and often brought home shells, butterfly wings, colored stones, and other objects that he collected about him. He was fascinated by the growth of plants and their manifestations of sexuality (*Figure 41*).

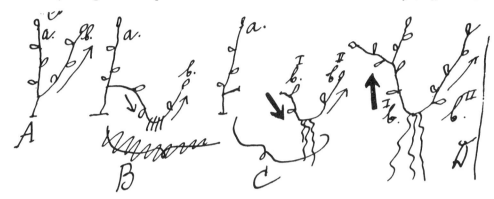

Figure 41. "A neat experiment in the field of capillary action." After the branch "*b*" is bent down, becomes rooted, and is cut off from "*a*," the direction of circulation of sap is reversed. (From Klee, *Diaries*, 1964, p. 204; reproduced by permission of the University of California Press.)

Klee's botanical interests figure prominently in his art. *Male and Female Plant* (1921) (Plate 2) is a wonderful example of his deep interest in nature, as is the *Botanical Theater* (1934). In his teaching he assigned special value to buildings and other architectural works because their elements could be so readily analyzed and a "spatial organism" could be calculated. Once the artist grasps the idea of measurability in connection with design, "the study of nature will progress with greater ease and accuracy."

The richness of nature, of course, is so much the greater and more rewarding by reason of its infinite complexity.

Our initial perplexity before nature is explained by our seeing at first the small outer branches and not penetrating to the main branches or the trunk. But once this is realized, one will perceive a repetition of the whole law even in the outermost leaf and turn it to good use.[7]

[6] Klee, *Diaries* (1964), p. 98. *Hanging Fruits* (1921) is a striking example of his interest in crystal forms and their potential relationship to organisms — in Grohmann, *Paul Klee* (1955), p. 165.

[7] *Ibid.*, pp. 146-147, December 1903 (quotations by permission of the University of California Press). *Fish Magic* (1925), Grohmann (1955), p. 210, is a wonderfully evocative composition of fishes and plant forms in an aquarium-like setting. See also Felix Klee, *Paul Klee: His Life and Work in Documents* . . . (New York: George Braziller, 1962), pp. 176-7.

Klee had grasped the essential character of organic forms, the primacy of the total organism, and he tried to develop a system of art in which the simplest elements might be combined so as to suggest emergent order. Charles Bouleau discerns in Klee's career a number of stages of which the earliest is characterized by crystalline or prismatic compositions. Klee then progressed to "coralline compositions, with their organic, articulated, and sinuous development." (Corallines are colonial, usually stalked or branched, sea animals.) *Cacti* (1913) is a study of cells in series and layers. *The Fruit* (1929) shows the external form of a fruit with layers of internal strata and a core, shapes revealed by the progressive coil of a spiral line whose course, like the analytic diagram of the morphologist, recapitulates the process of growth. Many of Klee's compositions remind us of Keats' expressions of the organic affinities of the spirit of poesy.

In the Meadow (1923) is divided into fourteen layers by curving horizontal lines spaced at irregular intervals within which the heads and bodies of human bodies are disposed like drawings in a treatise on proportion. Their anatomy conforms precisely to the lines in a manner that suggests an array of plants in a scientific drawing. But we realize that the plants derive their life from the rhythmic interplay of the verticals and horizontals by which they are defined, set not at constant intervals but with a variety that elevates the space-lattice above the crystalline into the realm of organic order.[8] Klee's love for the plants and fishes that figure so prominently in his paintings stems from their value to his overall artistic program. He employed them as emblems of the idea of organic form that had guided him in his search for the principles of visual expression.

Wassily Kandinsky (1866-1944) had worked in Paris where he was strongly influenced by Gauguin and Matisse. Upon his return to Munich he lived next door to Klee and invited him to join the Blue Rider group of expressionists formed in 1912, to which Franz Marc and Hans Arp also belonged. In an important pronouncement written in 1910, *On the Spiritual in Art,* he expounded a theory of forms which seems to have guided his career as an artist. Rather than imitate the external forms of nature, which he compared to trying to recreate the sound of the chicken farm in music, the aim of art should be to represent the innermost quality of nature, its atmosphere. Neoclassicism, in attempting to improve upon external form, only "dampened its inner personal sound." If one properly attends to the organic form an inner sound may be heard, "an element of the divine message." This inner note of the natural object may be heard even if the exterior aspect is not represented. The invention of forms in art should be governed by their potential to induce "correspond-

---

[8] Bouleau, *The Painter's Secret Geometry* (1963), p. 239, with a black-and-white reproduction of *In the Meadow* (1923), also figured in Grohmann (1955), p. 173. Also see Nierendorf, *Paul Klee* (1941) for similar space-defining lattices in *Arrival of the Acrobats* (1920), or *Children Arrive at the City* (1929).

ing vibration of the human soul." A painting may start from a single point and then develop from *inner necessity*, expressing the artist's sense of the "innermost organic variations" of individual forms. Kandinsky's paintings from these years (1911-1915) almost all include separate abstract elements whose exterior is rounded, ramified into threads, or swollen into a protrusion as though some vital fluid pressed upon a membrane surface.[9] *Small Pleasures* (1913) and *White Edge* (1913) contain numerous form elements seemingly imbued with the potency of change; we expect them to flow or extend like parts of a tissue culture (that technique was invented by Ross Granville Harrison in 1910).[10] Kandinsky's work in the 1930s and 1940s acquires an explicit biological quality. The forms best suited to his expressionist program are those of organisms, protozoa, and other microscopic life, as in *Capricious Forms No. 643* (1937).[11] (Plate 4)

Klee and Kandinsky employed in their art forms and spatial concepts that reflect a conscious awareness of the distinction between organic and inorganic structures. The idea of organic form was directly relevant to their artistic programs. Given the original esthetic character of the idea of organic form, its adoption in the revolutionary program of twentieth-century abstract art did not entail a change in the frame of reference of the visual arts, only a reorientation within it. Works of art continued to be referred to an esthetic principle, and one of long standing at that. This reference did not consist of a direct borrowing from science, but it did represent an unusual conjunction between scientific and artistic procedures, a rather infrequent occurrence in the constellation of western culture; however, the reasons for the currency of the idea of organic form in these two realms of culture were quite different. In science it was an instrument of discovery, the basis of an explanatory paradigm, which would be set aside if it lost its predictive value regarding problems under investigation, while its life in art reflects its relevance to the difficulties experienced by painters and sculptors in expressing their values and feelings.

It would be a mistake, I believe, to limit the influence of the idea of organic form in art to documented instances of copying from scientific treatises. Literalism of this kind usually bespeaks a lack of talent or a naturalism that the twentieth-century artist does not acknowledge. The forms employed by the artist have been used successfully if they have been transmuted into a heightened

[9] See Barr, *Cubism and Abstract Art,* the catalogue of the Museum of Modern Art exhibition of 1936, for *Improvisation* (1915), p. 18, and *Composition No. 1* (1921), p. 69.
[10] Kandinsky, *On the Spiritual in Art* [1911], reproduced at pp. 115-116. See also *Composition VI* and *Composition VII* in Bouleau, *op. cit.,* pp. 234-235.
[11] See *Composition No. 678* (1940), p. 123; *Around the Line* (1943), p. 124; and *Well-Tempered Emphasis* (1944), p. 125, in *On the Spiritual in Art* [1911]. There is a concise statement of Kandinsky's theory of art in Blanshard, *Retreat from Likeness in the Theory of Painting* (1945), pp. 74-79. Also see the very remarkable and early abstract work by Leopold Stoba, *Formation* (1906), clearly influenced by cytological cross sections, in Berckelaers, *Abstract Painting* (1962), p. 8.

state of being with the results that they enter readily into a creative program.

We may find a highly satisfactory account of the transmutation of visual form in J. Livingston Lowes' masterly portrayal of the imaginative process of creation by which Coleridge arrived at the previously cited key passage of the *Ancient Mariner*. Lowes discovered evidence in a notebook that Coleridge had read Joseph Priestley's writings on the phosphorescent tracks of fish, Sir William Dampier's observations on water snakes at sea, and the description of innumerable jellyfish or salps in the Pacific by Captain Cook, but he cautioned that these scientific sources yielded only raw materials still to be "transmuted into elements of beauty." The elements of art were first combined in a subconscious stratum of the mind, "like nothing else in the world so much as a jungle, illuminated eerily with patches of phosphorescent light, and peopled with uncanny life and strange exotic flowers. But it is teeming and fecund soil, and out of it later rose, like exhalations, gleaming and aerial shapes." [12] It seems that Coleridge's imagination revealed a predisposition toward expression in organic forms.

We may regard the prominence of visual and esthetic factors in biology as evidence that this science has benefited from privileged access to the substrate of the mind whence organic forms arise. Before the fine structure of the endings of nerve cells had been properly observed, it was widely believed that their terminations were interconnected in a network of protoplasm. This belief was reinforced by the idea that muscle fibers were composed of a tiny latticework of delicate contractile elements in a network pattern. This notion of a universal network structure in living tissue, which we have already encountered in Bütschli, proved highly seductive and was held by numerous investigators in the 1870s and 1880s. The Spaniard Santiago Ramón y Cajal (1852-1934), co-winner of the Nobel Prize for Medicine in 1906, had accepted the network theory as a young man. He observed that such "simple schemes stimulate and appeal to tendencies deeply rooted in our minds, the congenital inclination to economy of mental effort and the almost irresistible propensity to regard as true what satisfies our esthetic sensibility by appearing in agreeable and harmonious architectural forms. As always, reason is silent before beauty." [13] These esthetic presuppositions had been given scope in the process of interpretation, which begins where the observed facts end. The field of histology was subject to special difficulties in this respect, not only because its investigators often worked at the very limits of microscopic vision, but because they employed preparations that had been fixed or stained in ways that could cause changes in apparent structure. Despite these many uncertainties, the progress of factual discovery was maintained and slowly overtook conjectural interpretations. Cajal's own

[12] Lowes, *The Road to Xanadu* (1927), p. 6. On Coleridge's visual faculty, see "The Falcon's Eye," pp. 32-37 and 66-70.
[13] Ramón y Cajal, *Recollections of My Life* (1937), vol. II, p. 303.

future role was highly interesting in view of his strictures on esthetic presuppositions, quoted above. In 1888 he demonstrated that the axons of nerves do not form a continuous diffuse network, but ramify to discrete points of contact (synapses). He traveled to the German Anatomical Congress in 1889 and showed his preparations to all of the leading cytologists in a triumphant display that dispelled the network hypothesis[14] (*Figure 42*).

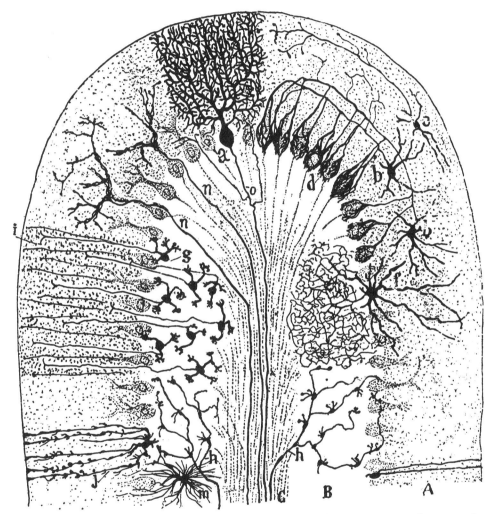

Figure 42. A schematized transverse section of different cell types in a convolution in the mammalian cerebellum, drawn by Cajal in 1894. This drawing gives a vivid impression of the complexity of the cellular processes and the detailed nature of Cajal's demonstration of arborizations rather than networks. (From Ramón y Cajal, *Recollections of My Life*, 1937, vol. II, p. 333, fig. 28.)

[14] *Ibid.*, pp. 321-332 and 354-359; also Liddell, *The Discovery of Reflexes* (1960), pp. 1-30.

So he succeeded in overcoming his youthful attachment to the network concept and contributed to the establishment of a new empirical reality, the neuron
as a structural unit. And yet it becomes apparent from reading his autobiography
that Cajal was obsessed by the beauty of these tissues. He had aspired to become
an artist in childhood and throughout his scientific career he lavished attention
on the drawings he prepared for his papers. His recovery from initial error about
muscle structure makes it plain that progress in science calls for vigilant control
of subjectivity, wherein lies a crucial difference between art and science. The
esthetic factor in science is harnessed to the service of critical faculties, but its
scope is vast nonetheless. In spite of all his cautions about yielding to the sense
of beauty, Cajal recorded that his anatomical studies afforded him "delicious
rapture, an irresistible enchantment."

The garden of neurology holds out to the investigator captivating spectacles and
incomparable artistic emotions. In it, my esthetic instincts found full satisfaction at
last. Like the entomologist in pursuit of brightly colored butterflies, my attention
hunted in the flower garden of the gray matter, cells with delicate and elegant
forms, the mysterious butterflies of the soul, the beating of whose wings may some
day—who knows?—clarify the secret of mental life.[15]

The golden section, the irrational ratio which had fascinated plant mor-
phologists by its apparent peculiarity to organic forms, was introduced to the
Paris art world by the theorist and painter Paul Sérusier (1863-1927), who
became in 1908 one of the principal teachers at the Académie Ranson.[16] The
Cubist Jacques Villon and the brothers Duchamp, along with several others,
formed the *Salon de la Section d'or* in 1912. Such theoretical formulations as
Matila Ghyka's *Le Nombre d'or, Rites et rhythmes pythagoriciens* (1931), and
André Lhote's *Parlons peinture* (1936) amplified this interest, and the golden
section became one of the dominant compositional principles in the work of Piet

<hr>

[15] *Ibid.*, p. 363. Thus, Polanyi observes, in *Personal Knowledge* [1958], p. 194: "The arts
appear then no longer as contrasted but as immediately continuous with science." Victor C.
Twitty, *Of Scientists and Salamanders* (San Francisco: W. H. Freeman, 1966), pp. 9-10,
writes of his former teacher, the distinguished embryologist Ross Granville Harrison, as
follows: "If I had to identify a single factor that made Harrison's work great, I would do
it in terms of esthetic considerations. He was constitutionally incapable of leaving a project
until all its pieces had been fitted into a unitary whole whose composition met his artistic
requirements." Konrad Lorenz has written that no one could bring to bear on animals the
powers of concentration required for the analysis of behavior "unless his eyes were bound
to the object of his observation in that spellbound gaze which is not motivated by any
conscious effort to gain knowledge, but by that mysterious charm that the beauty of living
creatures works on some of us." "Physiological Mechanisms in Animal Behavior," *Symposia
of the Society for Experimental Biology*, no. 4 (Cambridge, 1950), p. 235. See also
C.F.A. Pantin on "esthetic recognition" in "The Recognition of Species," *Science Progress*,
vol. 42 (1954), p. 587; also Ragnar Granit, *Charles Scott Sherrington: An Appraisal*
(New York: Doubleday, 1967), p. 176; also Karl Pearson, *The Grammar of Science* (London: Adam and Charles Black, 1900), pp. 13-15.
[16] Sérusier, *ABC de la peinture* [1921] (Paris: Floury, 1942), pp. 16-20, with an essay
by Maurice Denis, "Paul Sérusier: sa vie son œuvre," pp. 37-121.

Mondrian (1872-1944), who was opposed to the representation of anything from the more accessible categories of human experience. Mondrian exemplifies a subtle indebtedness to the biologists who had contributed to the enhanced esthetic standing of organic form.[17]

The greatest influence of the idea of organic form in the visual arts was its contribution to the Surrealist Movement from 1920 to 1947 and to its successors. In 1921 Max Ernst (b. 1891) produced his collage *The Sandworm Attaches Its Sandal,* a rhythmic progression of shells and latticework figures representing transmutations that would be impossible except within the substratum of unconsciousness wherein organic forms reside. From this time also dates *The Gramineous Bicycle,* a gouache made up of cells cut from an anatomical chart, a witty composition which is imbued with vitality. His sheaf of thirty-four drawings published under the title *Histoire Naturelle* in Paris in 1926 begins by exploiting the tensions between elementary spheres and ambient fluids, then presents images of flowing lines of force and incipient crystallization, elementary networks and articulations, and progresses to emergent living order in sheaths, canopies, and membranes. His *Gulf Stream and Bird* (1926) and *The Blind Swimmer* (1934) show confluent wave patterns charged with energy and vitality; in the center of *The Blind Swimmer* is a kernel with rhythmic articulations like a cell undergoing division.[18] His frontispiece for a 1963 reprint of Grandville's *Un autre monde* (1844) shows an articulated spiral, the form of the chambered nautilus, mysteriously suspended in space.[19] Joan Miró (b. 1893), a longtime adherent of the Surrealist Movement, included in his elegant compositions the forms of ciliated protozoa, flowing protoplasmic entities with pseudopods, and surfaces with flagella. In *Terre Labourée* (1923) and *Le Chasseur* (1924) the figures of familiar macroscopic animals are transformed into the simpler filiform and cell outlines of the microscopic realm.[20] Much Surrealist art consists of experimentation designed to stretch our ability to recognize familiar forms to the breaking point; their form is organic but there are features of the work which we refuse to acknowledge. Much of the dramatic quality of Surrealist art arises through this kind of negative experiment.

In the works of André Masson (b. 1896) interpenetrating globules, curves, and filaments arise from fluid backgrounds imbued with energy. He wrote that there was "no hierarchy in the cycle of natural forms. The royal structure of the human body is no more beautiful than the radiolaria, an oceanic star with

[17] Bouleau, *The Painter's Secret Geometry* (1963), pp. 245-251.
[18] Ernst, *Beyond Painting* (1948), and Rubin, "Toward a Critical Framework" (1966), p. 47. See also Warner Haftmann, *German Art of the Twentieth Century* (New York: Museum of Modern Art, 1957), p. 90.
[19] Ernst, "Un nouveau monde est né—que GRANVILLE soit loué," in Jean-Isidore Gerard [Grandville], *Un autre monde* (Paris: Les Libraires Associés, 1963). (Reproduced for the jacket illustration of this book by permission of Les Libraires Associés.)
[20] Bréton, *Le Surréalisme et la peinture* (1945), plates following p. 64.

solid rays."[21] One of the greatest Surrealist paintings is the *Vertige d'Eros* of Matta (b. 1911), reproduced as frontispiece to this book, within whose deep fluid spaces appear planes and intersections portentous of life, ovoid germs, pulsing figures, and nascent protoplasmic entities. The paintings of Yves Tanguy (b. 1900) figure profusions of biological images, generalized protozoa, amoeboid shapes of gelatinous substance, and forms with tentacles trailing in ambient fluid.[22] In his catalogue of the Baziotes exhibit at the Guggenheim, Lawrence Alloway wrote that Tanguy's images "resemble the blossoms of sea anemones, octopi-derivatives, and amoebic cells."[23] Pavel Tchelitchew (1898-1957) wrote of an "inner landscape" within man which he sought to express by allegorical painting "reflecting in its nature and properties the microcosm of the infinitely small world of biology."[24] Lawrence Kupferman, one of a number of contemporary painters who continue to exploit the world of organic forms, finds that these forms retain their expressiveness. He wrote of his own works, "My purpose in doing these paintings based on microscopic life and other aspects of biology and botany is to rediscover anew, for myself, the elements of the universe. Divorced from conventional reality (as of a still life, a landscape, a human figure), out of the minute world of the microscope I can find symbols of universal growth and life."[25]

A few perceptive critics have written about the biological character of these forms. Alfred Barr has distinguished two currents in abstract art: the first, geometrical and rectilinear, linking Cézanne, the Cubists, and Mondrian; and the second linking Gauguin, Matisse, Kandinsky, and the Surrealists. "This tradition, by contrast with the first, is intuitional and emotional rather than intellectual; organic or biomorphic rather than geometrical in its forms . . . ."[26] A leading student of Surrealist art, Professor William Rubin, finds biomorphic form "a major

[21] Masson, *Anatomy of My Universe* (New York: Curt Valentin, 1943).

[22] Works of these artists are reproduced in Barr, *Cubism and Abstract Art* (1936); Bréton, *Le Surréalisme et la peinture* (1945); Guggenheim, *Art of This Century* (1942); Rubin, *Dada and Surrealist Art* (1968); Janis, *Abstract & Surrealist Art in America* (1944), especially pp. 102-104. Also see in Schwabacher, *Arshile Gorky* (1957), the *Image of Xhorkom* paintings (1936), pls. 14, 18, and 19.

[23] Alloway, *William Baziotes: A Memorial Exhibition* (New York: Solomon R. Guggenheim Foundation, 1965), p. 11.

[24] In Edouard Roditi, *Dialogues on Art* (New York: Humanities Press, 1960), p. 125 (quoted by permission of the Humanities Press).

[25] Kupferman, in *Contemporary American Painting and Sculpture* (University of Illinois, College of Fine and Applied Arts, 1953), p. 195 (quoted with his permission). See also R. H. Wilenski, *The Meaning of Modern Sculpture* (London: Faber and Faber, 1932), pp. 158-59.

[26] Barr, *Cubism and Abstract Art* (1936), p. 19; also note his comparison of compositions by Malevich and Kandinsky as examples of these contrary trends: "The shape of the square confronts the silhouette of the amoeba." See also Marcel Duchamp's *The Bride* (1912), fig. 41, p. [53].

common denominator—perhaps the only one—which allows us to draw together the stylistic innovations of the Surrealist years." [27] In the Surrealism of the twentieth century, as in the Romanticism of the nineteenth, the organism both symbolizes the creative act and expresses a central truth of art. [28]

Max Ernst cutting up an anatomy chart or André Masson copying from the Monod-Herzen text on morphology seem to be conspicuous examples of art becoming indebted to science. But this ignores the fact, shown so often in our glimpses of the history of morphology, that the science of biology had appropriated organic form, as we have defined it, from the repertory of esthetic principles. Again and again at decisive turning points in its history, biology has adopted the esthetically satisfying interpretation of a problem that acknowledged the effect within the organism of principles of emergent order serving to distinguish its form from inert structures. Organismal concepts of symmetry elucidated the phylogeny of invertebrates. The search for globules led to the cell. The recognition of symmetrical invariance in chromosomes opened the way to molecular genetics. The biological imagery of expressionism arises not from the factualness of science through the copying of illustrations but from the aspirations toward beauty that science and art hold in common.

In a very perceptive commentary Leo Steinberg has written about the affinities between science and abstract art:

Wittingly, or through unconscious exposure, the nonobjective artist draws much of his iconography from the visual data of the scientist—from magnifications of minute natural textures, from telescopic vistas, submarine scenery and X-ray photographs. Not that he undertakes to render a particular bacterial culture or pattern of refracted light. The shapes of his choice are recruited in good faith for their suggestiveness as shapes, and for their obscure correspondence to his inner state. But it is significant how often the morphology he finds analogous to his own sentient being is such as has revealed itself to human vision scientifically multiplied. It is apparently in these gestating images, shapes antecedent to the visible, that many abstract painters recognize an intenser mode of natural truth. On these uncharted realms of form they must impose esthetic unity; from them they wrest new decorative principles—such as the "biomorphic" motif in modern ornament and applied design. Nature they imitate no less than did Masaccio. But where the Renaissance had turned to nature's display windows, and to the finished forms of man and beast, the men of our time descend into nature's laboratories.[29]

[27] Rubin, "Toward a Critical Framework" (1966), p. 46.
[28] Thus, Hans Arp, the creator of orphic shapes such as *Human Concretion* (1935), wrote in a frequently quoted passage: "Art is a fruit growing out of a man like the fruit out of a plant, like the child out of the mother." ("Notes from a Diary," *Transition*, no. 21, Paris, 1932).
[29] Steinberg, "The Eye Is a Part of the Mind" (1953), p. 210 (quoted by permission of the editors of *Partisan Review*).

Every work of art is the product of imagination and feeling; it manifests an integrity that is violated by being broken up into parts and an allusiveness that avoids reduction to propositional statement. In a general sense, all art is organic. Thus, Henry James wrote that "A novel is a living thing, all one and continuous, like any other organism, and in proportion as it lives will it be found, I think, that in each of the parts there is something of each of the other parts." [30] It was this more generalized concept of the organic which assumed such importance in the literary criticism of T. E. Hulme, I. A. Richards, and T. S. Eliot. Such unity of structure was the basic formal value of Aristotelian esthetics; it was important for Renaissance art and remains so today.

Romantic esthetic theory had added as special considerations to the general concept of structural unity the parallelism between biological growth and artistic creation and the awareness of principles of emergent order distinguishing organic from inorganic processes. The idea of organic form may thus be seen as a special derivative from a general tradition of long standing. The influence of the narrower concept was greatest in the formative years of abstract painting and with the Surrealist Movement. The works in the exhibit, as its title implies, show the influence of the idea in their individual motifs, the elements of composition. Some of the works reveal spatial relationships characteristic of emergent order or curved surfaces suggesting the properties of fluids in living systems. Less explicit are compositions which contrive to suggest the metabolic processes of life, a rhythmic succession of phases, metamorphosis and interaction with surroundings suggesting an environment. All of the works in the exhibit (see Plates) have been selected with reference to formal criteria which define the special concept of organic form rather than general unity of structure: primacy of the whole over the parts, the possibility of interpreting a given form as a stage in a process of growth or the result of the assimilation of diverse elements, the presence of the formative impulse within an entity rather than external to it, and the interdependence of parts. Thus the exhibit exemplifies organic forms with repeated reference to the formal properties that make them uniquely biological rather than simply manifestations of the interrelation of elements that characterizes the art of all styles.

Of course there remains the possibility that a painter makes an explicitly biological reference in the title of a work or takes advantage of these formal principles without meaning to express the idea of organic form. We abstract certain formal properties from the work and find that it may in consequence be referred to an esthetic idea. This does not exhaust the potentialities of the work, any more than the referral to Coleridge's scientific sources for the flaming track of water snakes exhausts their meaning in *The Ancient Mariner*. The idea of organic forms is only one of many sources for the phenomenal richness, formal

[30] James, *The Art of Fiction and Other Essays* (New York: Oxford University Press, 1948), p. 13.

inventiveness, and expressive quality of twentieth-century art.

One of the general shifts in the thought of the twentieth century has been a broadening in the theory of mind from a view based largely on sensation and association to a more comprehensive understanding of principles of symbol and meaning, expression and interpretation. The idea of organic form was especially well suited to Gestalt psychology, whose cardinal precept was that perception of the whole preceded apprehension of the parts. In her esthetic philosophy Suzanne K. Langer has drawn upon contemporary sources in psychology and the study of symbolism, and she gives an especially satisfactory portrayal of the expressive aspects of art. The form of the work "is subtly but entirely congruent with forms of mentality and vital experience, which we recognize intuitively as something very much like feeling." [31] The evocative or emotive power of the art work is traced to the existence within ourselves of certain organic predispositions toward the organization of experience, especially emotional experience. The artistic import of the form depends upon its role in our internal, organic psychology.

The necessity of "living form" for any rendering of psychical events rests simply on the fact that such events are the very concentration of life, acts in which the deeper rhythms of the organism, mainly unfelt, are implicated so that the dynamic structure of the individual is reflected in the forms of feeling.[32]

The artistic use of form, then, is a direct reflection of man's kinship with organic nature. Miss Langer supposes that this accounts for the popularity of "art books" devoted to photographs of natural objects, such as Prochnow's *Formenkunst der Nature* (1934), Blossfeldt's *Urformen der Kunst* (1928), and Feininger's *Anatomy of Nature* (1956). She also asserts that the representation of feeling in works of art makes them our most suitable means for investigating mental processes scientifically. Miss Langer has generalized the organic theory of creativity, based upon its affinities with life processes, so that it accounts not just for the appearance of organic motifs in art but for all of its expressive qualities. Thus in another of its aspects the special concept of organic form blends into the widest possible setting of esthetic ideas. The ultimate destiny of these ever widening identities is in propositions wherein biology and art become indistinguishable.[33]

Sir D'Arcy Wentworth Thompson (1860-1948), educated as a zoologist at Cambridge, was for over sixty years professor of natural history in the University of St. Andrews. He published a number of descriptive and anatomical publications on marine fauna and served, as Huxley had, as an inspector of fisheries. He was a superb classical scholar and prose stylist whose translation of Aristotle's

---

[31] Langer, *Mind*, vol. 1 (1967), p. 67.
[32] *Ibid.*, p. 152 (quotations by permission of the Johns Hopkins University Press).
[33] This extreme position was taken up by Weidlé, "Biology of Art" (1957), who argues that biology and art correspond entirely, stating, for example, that the microstructure of works of art consists of points of tension, which he compares to cells, and concluding that art works should be analyzed morphologically.

Historia Animalium (1910) is unlikely to be surpassed. He is now remembered as the author of a great classic in biology, the summary treatise on morphology treated from a mathematical standpoint, *On Growth and Form* (1917). Clifford Dobell, the protozoologist, has written that the book sets out no unique discoveries, that its great virtue is in its comprehensiveness of treatment, yet he nevertheless deems it "a work of art no less than of science." [34] The reason for the great influence of this book lies in the uncompromising quality of the scientific spirit with which Thompson approached its subject and the scope to which he was able to extend its argument, demonstrating the orderliness of virtually every realm of organic form. Size, surface-to-weight or volume relationships, and rates of growth received exacting mathematical analyses. Thompson steadfastly limited his discussion to "physical phenomena," which is to say that he referred organic forms to mathematical regularities in the expectation that doing so brought him closer to their causes and governing principles. With Thompson the process of the objectification of form was virtually completed. He explained how molecular-level forces such as surface tension largely dictate the form of very small organisms and the character of cellular processes such as mitosis, anticipating results that are still being communicated by embryologists and others.

D'Arcy Thompson reaffirmed the idea of organic form, which must not be thought inconsistent with his emphasis on the mechanical nature of causation in biology. He recognized that the formation of cells was subject to the primacy of the organism as a whole. "A continuous field of force, somehow shaping the whole organism, independently of the number, magnitude and form of the individual cells, which enter like a froth into its fabric, seems to me certainly and obviously to exist." [35] He gave a superb exposition of the principles of least surface that govern the forms of liquids and demonstrated their application to protozoa and medusae. He approvingly cited Leduc's experiments on gelatin layers and presented a marvellous review of forms that arise through the coming together of elastic solids, demonstrating some of the value inherent in Bütschli's foam model for the open space-lattice of protoplasm. He dismissed Haeckel's idea of "biocrystals" intermediate between inorganic crystals and organic secretions, preferring to account for radiolarian skeletons in terms of the properties of the surface film of the organism. "The symmetry which the organism displays seems identical with that symmetry of forces which results from the play and interplay of surface-tensions in the whole system." [36] He presented a remarkable account of the logarithmic spiral and the golden mean, cautioning that the fractions of phyllotaxis derive from "mathematical reasons" and do not depend upon

---

[34] Dobell, "D'Arcy Wentworth Thompson," *Obituary Notices of the Royal Society of London,* no. 18 (1949), p. 612.
[35] Thompson, *On Growth and Form* [1917], p. 345.
[36] *Ibid.,* p. 723.

any ideal factors. The power of mathematics to describe the forms of living beings was evidence that they were shaped by "dynamical principles," processes of a physical character but in the service of the peculiar spatial and formal properties of organisms. "For the harmony of the world is made manifest in Form and Number, and the heart and soul and all of poetry of Natural Philosophy are embodied in the concept of mathematical beauty." [37] D'Arcy Thompson did not seek to elevate natural forms to some transcendent level of ideal being where they would be secure beyond the reach of science. Rather he insisted that organic forms were within the grasp of scientific explanation. The reader senses no loss in the esthetic standing of the forms thus subjected to scientific analysis. If anything, as the positive response to Thompson's work among artists and estheticians should show, he enhanced their esthetic standing by demonstrating their lawfulness, symmetry, and dependence upon organic process. The ideal forms of the *Naturphilosophie* are no more, but, in their confirmed existence as empirical realities, the same forms, objectified, have gained greatly in their significance for art. The destiny of organic forms in art was conferred upon them by science.

The study of the fine structure of living systems meanwhile progressed toward ever greater capacity to interpret complexity in protoplasm and the cell nucleus. The superb drawing of the amoeba published by S. O. Mast of Johns Hopkins University in 1925, showing the overall organization of the single protozoan cell and its inclusions, may be compared with Leidy's drawing published in 1879 (*Figure 29,* above) to indicate the growing sophistication of studies of organic fine structure (*Figure 43*).

By the 1930s it had been established that protoplasm was not simply an emulsion, as Bütschli had supposed, in which tiny drops of one liquid are dispersed within another, but a substance of even greater complexity. Although it flows and displays other liquid properties, the primary components of protoplasm are long molecules of protein, among which fats and other liquids are dispersed as colloidal particles. These structural features are many times smaller in diameter than the average wavelength of light available for illumination in the optical microscope and thus not visible with that instrument. One consequence of this mode of organization is a maximum of surface area among the component phases of protoplasm, which accounts for its capacity for rapid metabolic action at high energies. Protoplasm is now represented as a complex assemblage of molecules of proteins, lipids, water, and dissolved substances [38] (*Figure 44*).

The fine structure of the cell has been ramified extensively by progress in cytology and its internal architecture is now recognized to be exceedingly

---

[37] *Ibid.,* pp. 1096-1097. See also C. M. Wardlaw, "Mathematical Relationships," in *Morphogenesis in Plants* (London: Methuen, 1952), pp. 73-90.
[38] Seifriz, "Alveolar Structure of Protoplasm" (1930) and *Symposium* (1942); also Frey-Wyssling, *Submikroskopische Morphologie des Protoplasmas* (1938); also Don W. Fawcett, *The Cell: An Atlas of Fine Structure* (Philadelphia: W. B. Saunders, 1966).

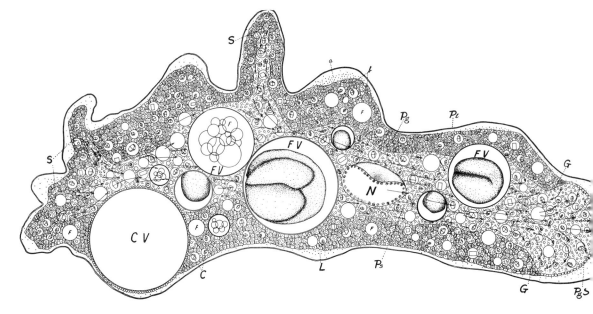

Figure 43. Horizontal section of *Amoeba proteus,* drawn at a magnification of approximately × 2000, showing two phases of protoplasm, a central fluid mass, the endoplasm, flowing forward as a sol enclosed by layers of gel. In the region of gelation, G, the somewhat fluid endoplasm becomes more viscous, forming the ectoplasmic layer that persists until it is reconverted at the posterior of the organism. N=nucleus; FV=food vacuoles; CV=contractile vacuole. (From Mast, "Structure, Movement, Locomotion, and Stimulation in Amoeba," *Journal of Morphology and Physiology,* vol. 41, 1925, pp. 363-4, fig. 1.)

Figure 44. Schematic representation of the ultrastructure of protoplasm. The smallest circles represent water amidst a network of long macromolecules of protein. At the lower left, a structure of concentric lamellae of lipids (fatty substances represented by short pinlike figures); lower right, a similar structure enclosing a drop of water; above, a glycerine droplet. The size of these spherical inclusions would be about 0.01μ to 0.05μ, ten times smaller than Bütschli supposed, and the individual molecules are in order of magnitude smaller. (From Albert Policard, *Histologie Physiologique,* 4th ed., Paris: G. Doin, 1944, fig. 7, p. 51.)

complicated. An atlas of electron photomicrographs such as Porter and Bonne-
ville's *Introduction to the Fine Structure of Cells and Tissues* (1964) brings
home with graphic effect the much finer texture taken on by explanations of the
cell. Most organelles within cells are made up of membranes now being interpreted successfully as molecular films. Thus, concepts of form have been brought
to bear directly upon theories of function at a new level of submicroscopic complexity, as in studies that seek to explain enzyme formation in terms of membrane
structure. The cell must not be treated as a vessel of chemically reacting liquids
but as a highly organized processing complex with a multitude of specialized
components *(Figure 45)*.

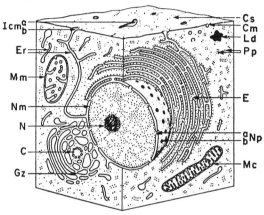

Figure 45. Diagram of an idealized segment of a cell approximately 1.5μ on a side: N=
nucleus; E and Er=endoplasmic reticulum; Ld=lipid droplet; C and Gz=Golgi particle;
Mc=mitochondrion with cristae. (From Pitelka, *Electron-Microscopic Structure of Protozoa*, 1963, fig. 1, p. 13; used by permission of the Pergamon Press.) Cf. Everett Anderson, "Cytoplasmic Organelles and Inclusions of Protozoa," in Tze-Tuan Chen, ed., *Research in Protozoology*, vol. 1 (Oxford: Pergamon Press, 1967), pl. 16.

It is at the level of ultrastructure that the celebrated double helix represents the
structure of DNA. James Watson has described his search for this structure as
being greatly reinforced by seeing helical staircases during a visit to Oxford. He
then looked through long series of electron photomicrographs of muscle and
collagen for instances of helical symmetry, as if to train his eye to analyze the
X-ray photographs of tobacco mosaic virus where he first recognized the helical
structure of RNA. His success in showing how base pairs could be assembled in
double-helix form demonstrated a new empirical reality and confirmed a presupposition of helical symmetry that "was too pretty not to be true." [39] Gradually
the breach that separated morphology and physiology in the nineteenth century
has been closed, at the level of molecular architecture, where form and function
are truly inseparable. The form of the cell components may be crystalline in

[39] Watson, "The Double Helix: The Discovery of the Structure of DNA," pt. II, *The
Atlantic*, vol. 221 (1968), p. 114.

certain respects, but it is clearer than ever that the organism as a whole cannot be regarded as a crystal-like structure. The systems of control and organization whereby the polypeptide chains of ultrastructure form organelles, cells, and tissues are only slightly known, and it is likely that the idea of organic form will continue to be of value in investigating these processes.

The great achievements of molecular biology in recent decades have been concentrated in the realm of function, such as the synthesis of proteins, and hardly at all in the elucidation of form. This has prompted a wave of criticism, much of it justified, from students of form who have advocated a broader approach with more frequent attention to general questions of form. The biologist Edmund Sinnott (1888-1968) has written:

Biologists are coming to realize that not simply metabolic changes, nor growth processes, nor gene action, nor the biochemical basis of living stuff provide the central problem of their science, but the way in which these phenomena are so interrelated that a *formed organism* is produced. The temporary ascendancy of one or another of these subdisciplines sometimes obscures this basic problem, but it always emerges again, in one aspect or another, as the one that biologists must solve if they are to understand what life really is. [40]

He listed the distinguishing properties of organic form as its basically fluid character, attributable to the properties of protoplasm, its reflection of processes that are constantly changing, and its manifestations of the coordinated control by the entire organism to which its parts are subject. It was upon these phenomena that Sinnott urged biologists to concentrate their investigations.

Joseph Needham (b. 1900) is a biochemist, a student of W. H. Hardy, who has already been cited for his interest in Coleridge as a philosophical biologist. Since World War II he has devoted himself to his epic history, *Science and Civilization in China*. His *Biochemistry and Morphogenesis* (1942) was an early and important work wherein he sought to demonstrate that a hierarchy of organizing relations guided the development of organisms, from the molecular and macromolecular levels to that of the organism as a whole. In *Order and Life* (1936), his Terry Lectures at Yale, he defined the aims of biological science as the explanation of the organism's primacy over its parts, its capacity to direct its growth, and to maintain its individuality: "The central problem of biology is the form problem." [41]

Conrad Waddington (b. 1905), an embryologist and geneticist of great distinction, has assigned a central place in his work to the problem of form. He has defined organic form as being individuated (being a property of entities deemed to be separable from one another), having a quality of completeness,

[40] Sinnott, *The Problem of Organic Form* (1963), pp. 8-9 (quoted by permission of the Yale University Press). See also "The Cell and the Problem of Organization" (1939).
[41] Needham, *Order and Life* (1936), p. 23 [reprinted M.I.T. Press, 1968]. Also a revealing early essay, "Organicism in Biology" (1928).

manifesting development, combining many functions in a single individual, and maintaining wholeness through the equilibrium of the numerous different forces by which the organism is sustained. "We come then to conceive of organic form as something which is produced by the interaction of numerous forces which are balanced against one another in a near-equilibrium that has the character not of a precisely definable pattern but rather of a slightly fluid one, a rhythm." [42] Waddington advocates a program of investigation aimed at understanding how these properties are maintained in a living system.

Paul Weiss (b. 1898) of the Rockefeller University, an eminent embryologist, has repeatedly urged his colleagues to devote greater attention to problems of form. He defines organic form as that which shows a high degree of regularity combined with freedom in details not strictly subject to the general pattern: emergent order arising within a system of interacting parts but not predictable from the information represented by those parts taken separately. [43] These formal attributes of living form may also be used to distinguish the living from the nonliving; they may serve as criteria for the interpretation of objects of unknown origin. Such criteria have been required for the analysis of the shapes of "organized entities" reported in meteorites, for example, or for minute fossils whose living origin has been doubted because of their great age. In defending his attribution of the microfossils of the well known Gunflint chert deposits, Preston Cloud has written, "the septate thread, the cellular-walled spheroid, and the perforate spheroid have, to my knowledge, never been produced without biologic intervention." [44] What these writers share is a sense of the continued relevance of the idea of organic form, the value for science of the recognition of formal properties distinguishing the living from the nonliving. They have joined in reaffirming a central esthetic tradition in biology and demonstrating its vitality as a guiding principle, a fertile source of the esthetic presuppositions whose continued contribution means so much to the life of science. The appearance of biomorphic elements in twentieth-century abstract art testifies to the esthetic value of the idea of organic form, its ability to infuse the concepts of science with the beauty that rewards all seekers after truth. The perpetuation of this central theme in the coming age of biological discovery will be undertaken by those biologists who wish to sustain the great heritage of their science and its central situation in our culture.

[42] Waddington, "The Character of Biological Form," in Whyte, ed., *Aspects of Form* (1951), p. 47. Waddington includes as illustrations of his conception of the "organic" several sculptures by Hans Arp and Henry Moore, which he seeks to distinguish from "nonorganic" works. He has written a history of twentieth-century art, forthcoming in 1968 from the M.I.T. Press, under the title *Behind Appearance*, which should be as interesting as a documentation of the vision of the biologist as it will undoubtedly be as a history of the perception of reality by artists.

[43] See especially Weiss, "One Plus One Does Not Equal Two" (1967).

[44] Cloud, "Significance of the Gunflint (Precambrian) Microflora," *Science,* vol. 148 (April 2, 1965), p. 32.

The Art of Organic Forms VI

A CATALOGUE OF THE EXHIBIT
Prepared by Diana Hamilton

(Dimensions are in inches; height precedes width)

Alo Altripp
born 1906, near Ludwigshafen, Germany
lives in Wiesbaden, Germany

"'Chopin"
1938
Oil on canvas
13½ x 19¼
Walter Inge Farmer, Cincinnati, Ohio

"Abstract Forms"
1957
Drawing, pencil
19 x 13½
Walter Inge Farmer, Cincinnati, Ohio

Jean (Hans) Arp
born 1887, Strasbourg, France
lives in Meudon, France

"Evocation humaine, lunaire spectrale"
1960
Bronze, one of an edition of three
18 height, including base
Dunkelman Gallery, Toronto, Ontario, Canada

"Nid-Enchanteur"
1965
Marble
25 height
Sidney Janis Gallery, New York City

Mary Bauermeister
born 1934, Frankfurt, Germany
lives in Madison, Connecticut

"Square Tree Commentaries"
1966
Lens box construction
30¼ x 30¼
Joseph H. Hirshhorn Collection, New York City

Willi Baumeister
born 1889, Stuttgart, Germany
died 1955, Stuttgart, Germany

"Growing"
Circa 1955
Oil and sand on canvas
40 x 30
Mrs. Charlotte Weidler, New York City

Herbert Bayer
born 1900, Haag, Austria
lives in Aspen, Colorado

"blue evolution" (Plate 15)
1955
Oil on canvas
32 x 40
Artist's collection, Aspen, Colorado

William Baziotes
born 1912, Pittsburgh, Pennsylvania
died 1963, New York City

"Moon Fantasy" (Plate 13)
1953
Oil on canvas
48 x 36
Mrs. Bernard F. Gimbel, Greenwich, Connecticut

"Pompeii"
1955
Oil on canvas
60 x 48
Museum of Modern Art, New York City
Mrs. Bertram Smith Fund

Leon Berkowitz
born 1919, Philadelphia, Pennsylvania
lives in Washington, D.C.

"Scent of Gorse Sunset"
1963/64
Oil on canvas
60 x 76
Henri Gallery, Washington, D.C.

Patricia Berlin
born 1919, Chicago, Illinois
lives in Glen Rock, New Jersey

"Nerve Cells"
1965
Oil on canvas
47 x 49
Artist's collection, Rockefeller University, New York City

Benjamin Blake
born 1928, Columbia, South Carolina
lives in San Francisco, California

Untitled
1965
Oil on canvas
47½ x 33½
Dr. John C. Harbert, Washington, D.C.

Lee Bontecou
born 1931, Providence, Rhode Island
lives in New York City and Paris, France

"Untitled"
1962
Construction in wire and canvas
31 x 34¼ x 13¾
Washington Gallery of Modern Art, Washington, D.C.
Gift of Mrs. Clive DuVal II

Richard Boyce
born 1920, New York City
lives in New York City

"Proteus Changing I"
1965
Unique bronze
14 height
Felix Landau Gallery, Los Angeles, California, and Landau-Alan Gallery,
   New York City

Sung Woo Chun
   born 1935, Seoul, Korea
   lives in Seoul, Korea

   "Mandala Tradition #2" (Plate 18)
   1964
   Oil on canvas
   50 x 44
   John Bolles Gallery, San Francisco, California

Michael Clark
   born 1946, Denver, Colorado
   lives in Washington, D.C.

   "Black Orchid"
   1966
   Acrylic on canvas
   36 x 42
   Evelyn Thurau, Washington, D.C.

Modest Cuixart
   born 1925, Barcelona, Spain
   lives in Barcelona, Spain

   "Argument" (Plate 20)
   1964
   Oil on canvas
   21½ x 15½
   Mr. and Mrs. Maurice Swergold, New York City

Arthur G. Dove
   born 1880, Canandaigua, New York
   died 1946, Centerport, New York

   "Life Goes On"
   1934
   Oil on canvas
   18 x 24
   The Phillips Collection, Washington, D.C.

Max Ernst
   born 1891, Bruhl, Germany
   became French citizen 1958
   lives in Paris, France

"Composition"
1924
Oil on canvas
10½ x 9
Mrs. Barnett Malbin, Birmingham, Michigan
The Lydia and Harry Lewis Winston Collection

"Histoire Naturelle"
1926
A portfolio of 34 colotypes after collages, published in Paris 1926
16⅞ x 10⅜ (composition variable)
Museum of Modern Art, New York City
Gift of Abby Aldrich Rockefeller

"Prenez garde au microbe de l'amour"
1949
Collage: colored crayon and two "microbe" oils
10½ x 8½
Muriel Bultman Francis, New Orleans, Louisiana

Lee Gatch
born 1902, Baltimore, Maryland
lives in Lambertville, New Jersey

"Flyway"
1954
Oil on canvas
42 x 30
The Phillips Collection, Washington, D.C.

Herbert George
born 1940, Seattle, Washington
lives in New York City

"Dance like a Comma"
1966
Canvas and wood
34 x 68 x 52
Stable Gallery, New York City

Arshile Gorky
born 1904, Khorkom Vari Haiyotz Dzor, Armenia
died 1948, Sherman, Connecticut

"Garden in Sochi" (Plate 5)
1938/42
Oil on canvas
31½ x 38¼
Estate of Arshile Gorky
Courtesy of M. Knoedler and Company, Incorporated, New York City

Drawing, study for "Summation" (Plate 9)
Pencil and crayon on paper
18½ x 24½ (sight)
Whitney Museum of American Art, New York City
Gift of Mr. and Mrs. Wolfgang S. Schwabacher

Drawing, study II for "Agony"
1946/47
Pencil and wax crayon on paper
19 x 25
Estate of Arshile Gorky
Courtesy of M. Knoedler and Company, Incorporated, New York City

Beatrice B. Grover
  born New York City
  lives in New York City

  "'Vulcan"
  1965
  Oil on canvas
  48 x 48
  Artist's collection, New York City

Catharine Homan
  born 1944, Washington, D.C.
  lives in Essex Falls, New Jersey

  "Porcelain Object"
  1968
  Porcelain and wood
  5 x 14 x 14
  Artist's collection, Essex Falls, New Jersey

Philippe Hosiasson
  born 1898, Odessa, U.S.S.R.
  lives in Paris, France

  Untitled
  1968
  Oil on canvas
  46 x 35
  Philippe Hosiasson, Paris, France

Hu Chi-chung
  born 1927, Chekiang, China
  lives in Taiwan, China

  "#6636"
  1966
  Oil on canvas
  39 x 28
  Lee Nordness Galleries, Incorporated, New York City

Fritz Hundertwasser
born 1928, Wien, Germany
lives in Paris, France

"Trampolin ins gelbe" (Plate 17)
1958
Mixed technique
36 x 33½
Julian J. Aberbach and Joachim Jean Aberbach, New York City

"La tour de Babel perce le soleil"
1959/60
Oil on paper mounted on burlap
51 x 63½
H. Marc Moyens, Alexandria, Virginia

Paul Jenkins
born 1923, Kansas City, Missouri
lives in New York City

"Lemur" (Plate 16)
1957
Oil on canvas
51¼ x 35
University of Kansas Museum of Art, Lawrence, Kansas

Walter Kamys
born 1917, Chicago, Illinois
lives in Montague, Massachusetts

"Seaquake" (Plate 10)
1948
Oil on canvas
36 x 40⅛
Yale University Art Gallery, New Haven, Connecticut
Gift of the artist for the Collection Société Anonyme

Vasily Kandinsky
born 1866, Moscow, U.S.S.R.
became French citizen 1939
died 1944, Neuilly-sur-Seine, France

"Capricious Forms No. 643" (Plate 4)
1937
Oil on canvas
35 x 45⅞
The Solomon R. Guggenheim Museum, New York City

Takeshi Kawashima
born Takamatsu, Japan
lives in New York City

"New Symbolism" (Plate 22)
1966
Liquitex on canvas
68 x 68
Aldrich Museum of Contemporary Art, Ridgefield, Connecticut

Leon Kelly
born 1901, Perpignan, France
lives in Harvey Cedars, New Jersey

"Departure through the Umbrellas" (Plate 7)
1944
Oil on canvas
22⅛ x 28
Whitney Museum of American Art, New York City
Gift of Briggs Buchanan

Gyorgy Kepes
born 1906, Selyp, Hungary
lives in Cambridge, Massachusetts

"Transformation"
1967
Oil and sand on canvas
Artist's collection, Cambridge, Massachusetts

Paul Klee
born 1879, Munchenbucksee, Switzerland
died 1940, Muralto-Locarno, Switzerland

"Weibliche und mannliche Pflanze" (Plate 2)
1921
Watercolor
8⅞ x 7 (not including paper margins)
Saidenberg Gallery, New York City

"The Familiars" (Family Matters among Fruit) (Plate 3)
1927
Drawing, pen
11¾ x 17¾
Jane Wade Lombard, New York City

Lawrence Kupferman
born 1909, Boston, Massachusetts
lives in Newton Centre, Massachusetts

"Tidal Maze"
1948
Watercolor
27 x 21
Artist's collection, Newton Center, Massachusetts

"Evolving Organic Forms"
1961
Oil on canvas
19 x 26
Artist's collection, Newton Center, Massachusetts

William Lumpkins
born 1935, Santa Fe, New Mexico
lives in Amherst, Massachusetts

Untitled
1967
Pencil and turpentine on paper
18 x 24
Artist's collection, Amherst, Massachusetts

Matta
born 1911, Santiago, Chile
lives in Paris, France

"Fabulous Racetrack of Death (Instrument Very Dangerous to the Eye)" (Plate 1)
No date
Oil on canvas
27½ x 35½
Yale University Art Gallery, New Haven, Connecticut
Collection of the Société Anonyme
Bequest of Katherine S. Dreier

"Composition Drawing (Personage Transparence)" (Plate 6)
Circa 1939
Oil pencil
19¼ x 25⅛
Wadsworth Atheneum, Hartford, Connecticut

"La lumiére complete"
1955
Oil on canvas
45¼ x 57⅛
Joseph H. Hirshhorn Collection, New York City

John Miró
born 1893, Barcelona, Spain
lives in Majorca, Balearic Islands, Spain

"Figures and Bird in Front of the Sun"
1930
Oil on unsized canvas
7⅝ x 10⁵⁄₁₆
Mrs. Barnett Malbin, Birmingham, Michigan
The Lydia and Harry Lewis Winston Collection

Untitled
1934
Ink and pastel on paper
17⅞ x 24⅛
Leon Berkowitz, Washington, D.C.

Untitled
1949
Mixed technique: oil, gouache, crayon
8¼ x 15
Mr. and Mrs. Alexander L. Berliner, New York City

Nuala [Elsa deBrun]
born 1896, Stockholm, Sweden
lives in New York City

"Either/Or #II" (Plate 21)
1964
Mixed media: pastel
17½ x 24
Artist's collection, New York City

"Either/Or #I" (Plate 23)
1967
Pastel and mixed media
21 x 28
Artist's collection, New York City

Guillermo Nuñez
born 1930, Santiago, Chile
lives in Santiago, Chile

"Break the Great Secret"
1964
Oil on canvas
49½ x 60
Mr. and Mrs. Samuel M. Greenbaum, Washington, D.C.

Georgia O'Keeffe
born 1887, Sun Prairie, Wisconsin
lives in Abiquiu, New Mexico

"From the Lake No. III"
1924
Oil on canvas
36 x 30
Artist's collection, Abiquiu, New Mexico

Jorge Piñeross
born 1929, Bogotá, Colombia
lives in Madrid, Spain

"Cellular Construction"
1967
Oil on canvas
31½ x 50½
Jorge Piñeross, Madrid, Spain
Courtesy the Pan American Union, Washington, D.C.

Odilon Redon
born 1840, Bordeaux, France
died 1916, Paris, France

"Au fond de la Mer"
Circa 1905
23⅞ x 19⅝
Mr. and Mrs. David Lloyd Kreeger, Washington, D.C.

Deborah Remington
born 1930, Haddonfield, New Jersey
lives in Paris, France, and New York City

"Haddonfield"
1965
Oil on canvas
74 x 69
Whitney Museum of American Art, New York City
Gift of the Friends of the Whitney Museum of American Art

Charles Seliger
born 1926, New York City
lives in Mount Vernon, New York

"Cerebral Landscape"
1944
Oil on canvas
24³⁄₁₆ x 18³⁄₁₆
Wadsworth Atheneum, Hartford, Connecticut

"Quanta" (Plate 19)
1964
Oil on canvas
30 x 40
Dr. and Mrs. H. G. Weitzen, New York City

Kurt Seligman
born 1900, Basle, Switzerland
lives in Sugar Loaf, New York

"Carnivorous Butterfly"
No date
Drawing
21 x 39
Mrs. Bernard J. Reis, New York City

Theodoros Stamos
  born 1922, New York City
  lives in New York City

  "The Thaw"
  Circa 1946/47
  Oil on masonite
  24 x 30
  Mr. Don Abarbanel, New York City

  "The Wedding" (Plate 12)
  1948
  Oil on masonite
  36 x 48
  Theodoros Stamos, New York City

Graham Sutherland
  born 1903, London, England
  lives in Menton, France

  "Thorn Head" (Plate 8)
  1945
  Chalk, ink, gouache
  22 x 21
  James Thrall Soby, New Canaan, Connecticut

  "Turning Form Number One"
  1948
  Chalk and gouache
  8¾ x 11
  Mr. and Mrs. John Henry Macdonell, Sarasota, Florida

Yves Tanguy
  born 1900, Paris, France
  became U. S. citizen 1948
  died 1955, Woodbury, Connecticut

  "The Storm" (L'Orage) (Black Landscape)
  1926
  Oil on canvas
  32 x 25¼
  Philadelphia Museum of Art, Philadelphia, Pennsylvania
  Louise and Walter Arensberg Collection

  "Titre inconnu"
  1927
  Oil on canvas
  21½ x 15
  Mr. and Mrs. Edward Bennett Williams, Washington, D.C.

  "Le regard de soie"

1940
Oil on canvas
18 x 15
Mr. and Mrs. David Lloyd Kreeger, Washington, D.C.

Pavel Tchelitchew
born 1898, District of Kalug near Moscow, U.S.S.R.
became U.S. citizen 1952
died 1957, Grotta Ferrata, Italy

"Itinerary of Light" (Plate 14)
1955
Oil on canvas
17½ x 18¾
Ruth Ford, New York City

Mark Tobey
born 1890, Centerville, Wisconsin
lives in Basle, Switzerland

"Geography of Phantasy" (Plate 11)
1948
Tempera
20 x 26
Mr. and Mrs. Olin J. Stephens II, Scarsdale, New York

Raoul Valdevieso
born 1931, Santiago, Chile
lives in Madrid, Spain

"Supplication"
1963
Bronze
21 x 17 x 4½
Mr. and Mrs. Samuel M. Greenbaum, Washington, D.C.

"Awakening of Earth"
1965
Bronze
28 x 18 x 8
Mr. and Mrs. Samuel M. Greenbaum, Washington, D.C.

Cyril Wilson
born 1911, High Wycombe, England
lives in Ibiza, Balearic Islands, Spain, and Dumpfriesshire, Scotland

"Seedhead Metamorphosis"
1967
Oil on canvas
30 x 40
Aitken Dott and Son, Edinburgh, Scotland

(Plate 1)

Matta

"Fabulous Racetrack of Death (Instrument Very Dangerous to the Eye)"
No date
Yale University Art Gallery, New Haven, Connecticut
Collection of the Société Anonyme

(Plate 2)

Paul Klee

"Weibliche und Mannliche Pflanze"
1921
John D. Schiff photograph

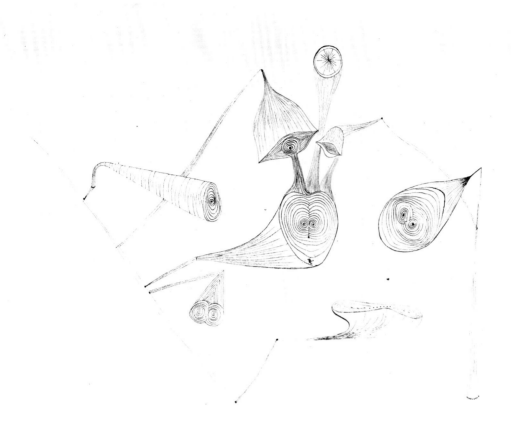

(Plate 3)

Paul Klee

"The Familiars"
1927

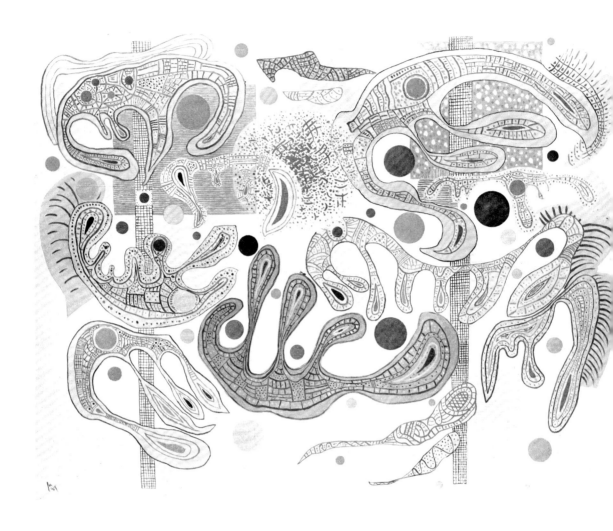

(Plate 4)

Vasily Kandinsky

"Capricious Forms No. 643"
1937
The Solomon R. Guggenheim Museum, New York City

(Plate 5)

Arshile Gorky

"Garden in Sochi"
1938/42
Paulus Leeser photograph

(Plate 6)

Matta

"Composition Drawing"
Circa 1939
Courtesy Wadsworth Atheneum, Hartford, Connecticut
W. F. Miller and Company photograph

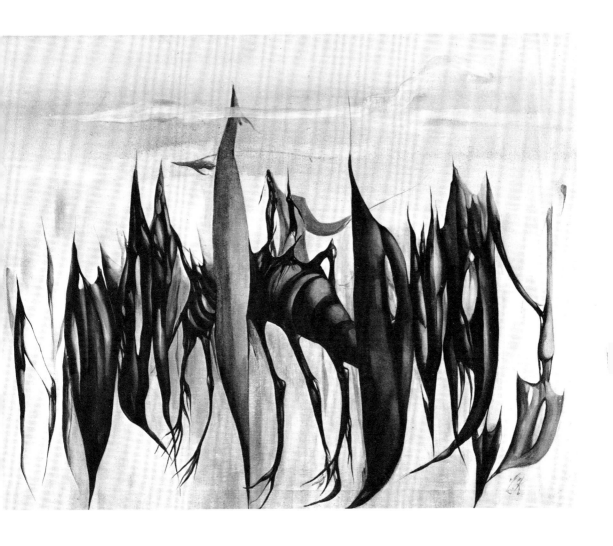

(Plate 7)

Leon Kelly

"Departure through the Umbrellas"
1944
Collection of the Whitney Museum of American Art, New York City

(Plate 8)

Graham Sutherland

"Thorn Head"
1945
The Museum of Modern Art, New York City
Soichi Sunami photograph

(Plate 9)

Arshile Gorky

Drawing, study for "Summation"
1946
Collection of the Whitney Museum of American Art, New York City
Gift of Mr. and Mrs. Wolfgang S. Schwabacher
Geoffrey Clements photograph

(Plate 10)

Walter Kamys

"Seaquake"
1948
Yale University Art Gallery, New Haven, Connecticut
Gift of the artist for the Collection Société Anonyme

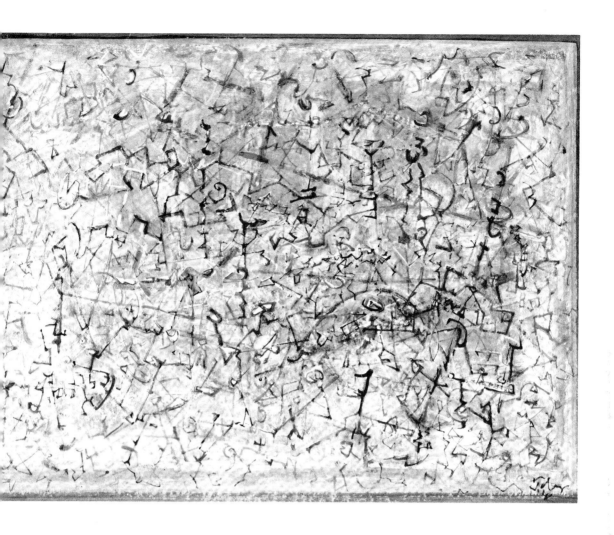

(Plate 11)

Mark Tobey

"Geography of Phantasy"
1948

(Plate 12)

Theodoros Stamos

"The Wedding"
1948
Geoffrey Clements photograph

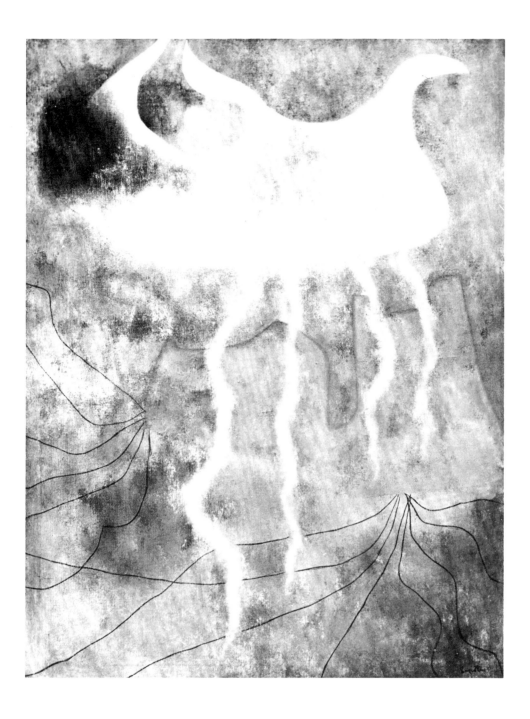

(Plate 13)

William Baziotes

"Moon Fantasy"
1953

(Plate 14)

Pavel Tchelichew

"Itinerary of Light"
1955
Geoffrey Clements photograph

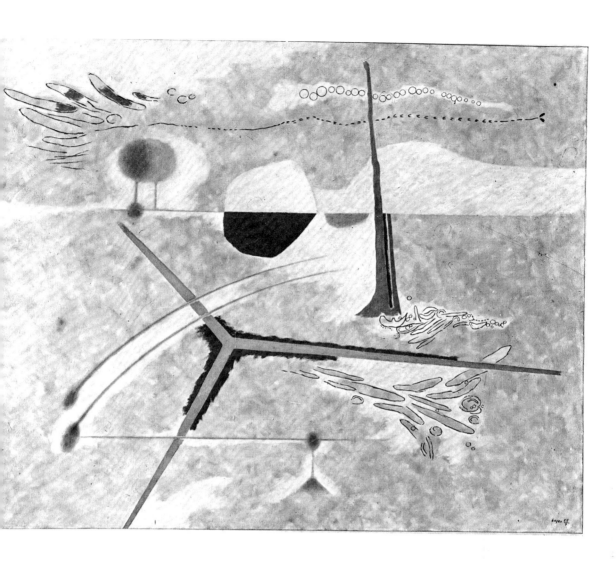

(Plate 15)

Herbert Bayer

"blue evolution"
1955/7

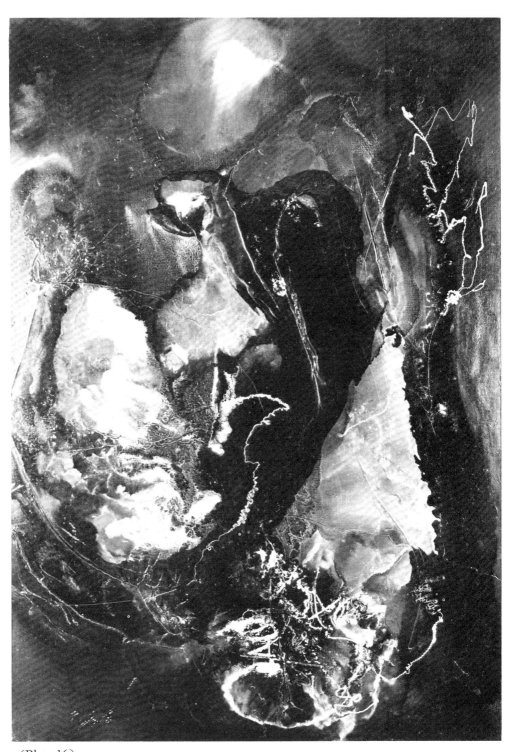

(Plate 16)

Paul Jenkins

"Lemur"
1957

(Plate 17)

Fritz Hundertwasser

"Trampolin ins Gelbe"
1958
Eric Pollitzer photograph

(Plate 18)

Sung Woo Chun

"Mandala Tradition #2"
1964

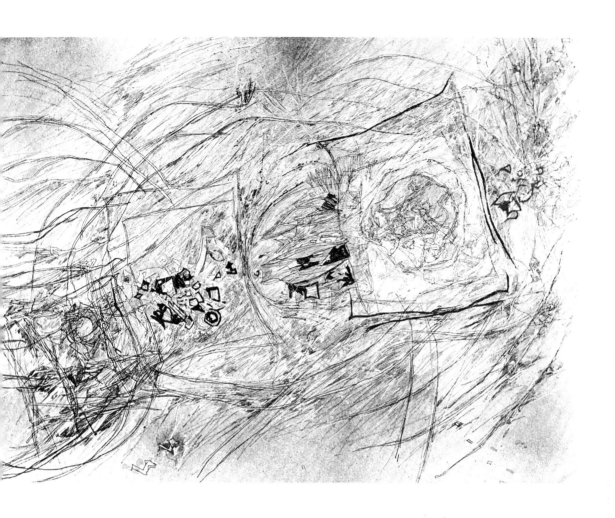

(Plate 19)

Charles Seliger

"Quanta"
1964
Frann Studios photograph

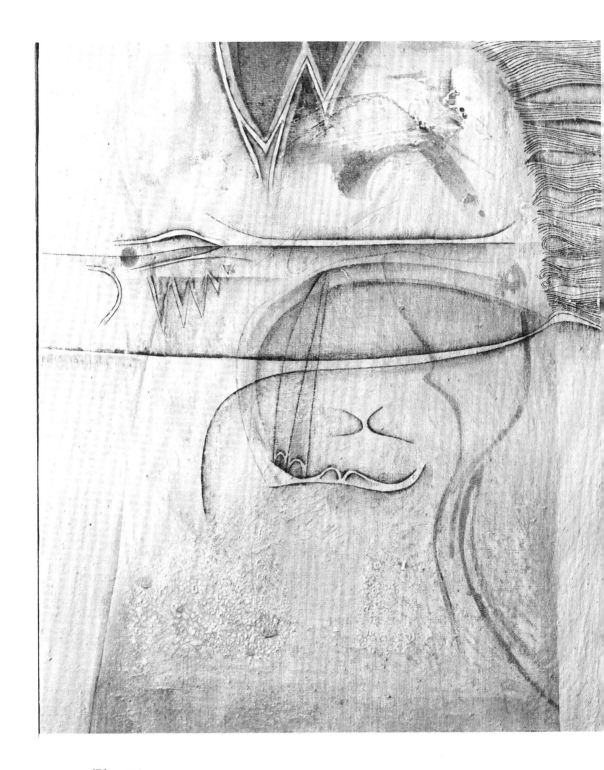

(Plate 20)

Modest Cuixart

"Argument"
1964

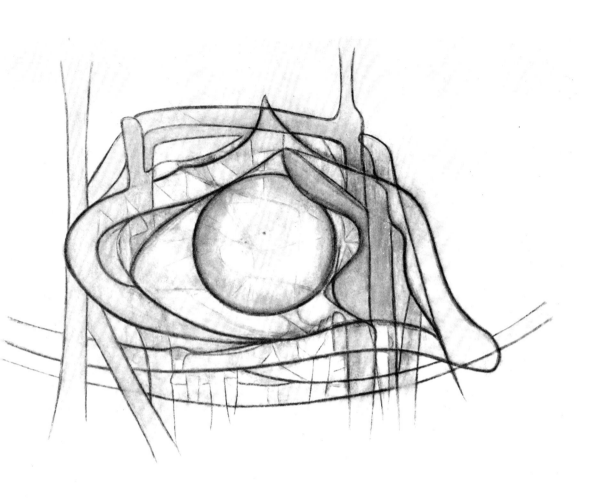

(Plate 21)

Nuala [Elsa deBrun]

"Either/Or #II"
1964
Geoffrey Clements photograph

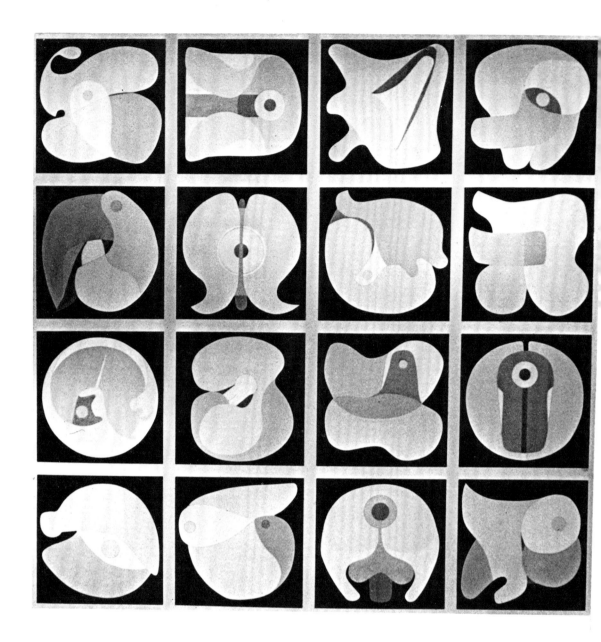

(Plate 22)

Takeshi Kawashima

"New Symbolism"
1966

(Plate 23)

Nuala [Elsa deBrun]

"Either/Or #1"
1967
Geoffrey Clements photograph

References

ABRAMS, MEYER HOWARD. The Mirror and the Lamp: Romantic Theory and the Critical Tradition. New York: Oxford University Press, 1953.

ANDREWS, GWENDOLEN FOULKE. The Living Substance: As Such and As Organism. (Supplement to *Journal of Morphology*, vol. 12.) Boston: Athenaeum Press, 1897.

APPLEYARD, J. A. Coleridge's Philosophy of Literature: The Development of a Concept of Poetry. Harvard University Press, 1965.

ARBER, AGNES. "Goethe's Botany," *Chronica Botanica*, vol. 10, no. 2 (1946), pp. 63-124.

──────. The Natural Philosophy of Plant Form. Cambridge University Press, 1950.

──────. The Mind and the Eye: A Study of the Biologist's Standpoint. Cambridge University Press, 1964.

AUDEN, W. H. The Dyer's Hand and Other Essays. New York: Random House, 1962.

BACOU, ROSELINE. Odilon Redon. . . . 2 vols. Geneva: Pierre Cailler, 1956.

BAUR, JOHN I. H. Nature in Abstraction. New York: Whitney Museum of American Art, 1958.

[BERCKELAERS, FERDINAND LOUIS]. Abstract Painting: Fifty Years of Accomplishment, from Kandinsky to the Present. New York: Harry N. Abrams, 1962.

BAKER, JOHN R. "The Cell Theory: A Restatement, History, and Critique." *Quarterly Journal of Microscopical Science,* vol. 89 (1948), pp. 103-125; vol. 90 (1949), pp. 87-108 and 331; vol. 93 (1952), pp. 157-189; vol. 94 (1953), pp. 407-440; and vol. 96 (1955), pp. 449-481.

BALTRUSAITIS, JURGIS. Réveils et prodiges: Le gothique fantastique. Paris: Armand Colin, 1960.

BALTZER, FRITZ. Theodor Boveri: Life and Work of a Great Biologist, 1862-1915 [1962]. Trans. Dorothea Rudnick. University of California Press, 1967.

BARNHART, EDWARD N.—See Chandler, Albert R.

BARR, ALFRED H., JR. Cubism and Abstract Art. . . . New York: Museum of Modern Art, 1936.

──────. Masters of Modern Art. New York: Museum of Modern Art, 1954.

BARRY, DAVID G. Art in Science. Albany, New York: Albany Institute of History and Art, 1965.

BEALE, LIONEL S. Protoplasm: or, Life, Matter, and Mind. 2nd ed. London: J. Churchill & Sons, 1870.

BENZIGER, JAMES. "Organic Unity: Leibniz to Coleridge." *PMLA Publications of the Modern Language Association of America,* vol. 66, no. 2 (March, 1951), pp. 24-48.

BERNAL, J. D. "Symmetry of the Genesis of Form." *Journal of Molecular Biology,* vol. 24 (1967), pp. 379-390, 5 pls.

BERTHOLD, GOTTFRIED. Studien über Protoplasmamechanik. Leipzig: Arthur Felix, 1886.

BLANSHARD, FRANCES BRADSHAW. Retreat from Likeness in the Theory of Painting. New York: King's Crown Press, 1945.

BLOSSFELDT, KARL. Art Forms in Nature: Examples from the Plant World Photographed Direct from Nature [1928]. New York: E. Weyhe, 1929.

BONNEVILLE, MARY A.—See Porter, Keith R.

BOULEAU, CHARLES. The Painter's Secret Geometry: A Study of Composition in Art. Trans. Jonathan Griffin. New York: Harcourt, Brace, and World, 1963.

BOYD, J. D., F. R. JOHNSON, and J. D. LEVER, eds. Electron Microscopy in Anatomy. Baltimore: Williams & Wilkins, 1961.

BRADBURY, SAVILE. The Evolution of the Microscope. Oxford: Pergamon Press, 1967.

BRAUN, ALEXANDER. "Vergleichende Untersuchung über die Ordnung der Schuppen an den Tannenzapfen als Einleitung zur Untersuchung der Blattstellung." *Nova Acta Physico-Medica Academiae Caesareae Leopoldino-Carolinae,* vol. 17 (1831), pp. 195-402 and 34 pls.

BRETON, ANDRÉ. Le surréalisme et la peinture suivi de genèse et perspective artistiques du surréalisme et de fragments inédits. New York: Brentano's, 1945.

BÜTSCHLI, OTTO. "Studien über die ersten Entwicklungsvorgänge der Eizelle, die Zelltheilung und die Conjugation der Infusorien." *Abhandlungen herausgegeben von der senckenbergischen naturforschenden Gesellschaft,* vol. 10 (1876), pp. 213-464 and 15 pls.

————. Ueber den Bau der Bacterien und verwandter Organismen. Leipzig: C. F. Winter'sche Verlagshandlung, 1890.

————. Untersuchungen über mikroskopische Schäume und das Protoplasma: Versuche und Beobachtungen zur Lösung der Frage nach den physikalischen Bedingungen der Lebenserscheinungen. Leipzig: W. Engelmann, 1892.

————. Untersuchungen über Strukturen insbesondere über Strukturen nichtzelliger Erzeugnisse des Organismus und über ihre Beziehungen zu Strukturen, welche ausserhalb des Organismus entstehen. With "Atlas." Leipzig: W. Engelmann, 1898.

BURKE, JOHN G. Origins of the Science of Crystals. University of California Press, 1966.

CANDOLLE, CASIMIR DE. Considérations sur l'étude de la phyllotaxie. Geneva: H. Georg, 1881.

CANGUILHEM, GEORGES. "The Role of Analogies and Models in Biological Discovery." *In* Alistair C. Crombie, ed., Scientific Change: Historical Studies in the Intellectual, Social and Technical Conditions for Scientific Discovery and Technical Invention, from Antiquity to the Present. . . . (New York: Basic Books, 1963), pp. 507-520.

————. La connaissance de la vie. 2nd ed. Paris: Librairie Philosophique J. Vrin, 1965.

CARPENTER, WILLIAM B. The Microscope and Its Revelations. 8th ed. Rev. by W. H. Dallinger. Philadelphia: P. Blakiston's Son, 1901.

CARRITT, EDGAR F. The Theory of Beauty [1914]. 2nd ed. London: Methuen, 1962.

CHANDLER, ALBERT R., and EDWARD N. BARNHART. A Bibliography of Psychological and Experimental Aesthetics, 1864-1937. University of California Press, 1938. [Mimeographed.]

COLE, FRANCIS JOSEPH. The History of Protozoology. . . . University of London Press, 1926.

COLERIDGE, SAMUEL TAYLOR. "On the Definitions of Life Hitherto Received: Hints Toward a More Comprehensive Theory" [1830]." *In* Miscellanies, Aesthetic and Literary: To Which Is Added the Theory of Life (London: George Bell and Sons, 1885), pp. 349-430.

COLMAN, SAMUEL. Nature's Harmonic Unity: A Treatise on Its Relation to Proportional Form. Ed. C. Arthur Coan. New York: G. P. Putnam's Sons, 1912.

COOK, THEODORE ANDREA. The Curves of Life: Being an Account of Spiral Formations and Their Application to Growth in Nature, to Science and to Art with Special Reference to the Manuscripts of Leonardo da Vinci. New York: Holt, 1914.

CROW, W. B. "Symmetry in Organisms." *American Naturalist*, vol. 62 (1928), pp. 207-227.

DAVY, SIR HUMPHREY. "Parallels between Art and Science" [1807]. *In* John Davy, ed., The Collected Works of Sir Humphry Davy, Bart . . . vol. 8 (London: Smith, Elder, 1840), pp. 306-309.

DÉRIBÉRÉ, MAURICE. Images étranges de la nature. Paris: Editions de Varenne [1951].

DUJARDIN, FELIX. Histoire naturelle des zoophytes: Infusoires, comprenant la physiologie et la classification de ces animaux, et la manière de les étudier a l'aide du microscope. Paris: Librarie Encyclopédique de Roret, 1841.

DUTROCHET, HENRI JOACHIM. Recherches anatomiques et physiologiques sur la structure intime des animaux et des végétaux, et sur leur motilité. Paris: J.-B. Ballière, 1824.

EHRENBERG, CHRISTIAN GOTTFRIED. Die Infusionsthierchen als vollkommene Organismen: Ein Blick in das tiefere organische Leben der Natur. Leipzig: Leopold Voss, 1838.

ERNST, MAX. Beyond Painting and Other Writings by the Artist and His Friends. ("The Documents of Modern Art," ed. Robert Motherwell.) New York: Wittenborn, Schultz, 1948.

EVANS, JOAN. Nature in Design: A Study of Naturalism in Decorative Art from the Bronze Age to the Renaissance. Oxford University Press, 1933.

FARÉ, MICHEL. La nature morte en France: Son histoire et son évolution du XVIIᵉ au XXᵉ siècle. Geneva: Pierre Cailler, 1962.

FEININGER, ANDREAS. The Anatomy of Nature: How Function Shapes the Form and Design of Animate and Inanimate Structures Throughout the Universe. New York: Crown, 1956.

FLORKIN, MAURICE. Naissance et déviation de la théorie cellulaire dans l'oeuvre de Théodore Schwann. Paris: Hermann, 1960.

FREY-WYSSLING, ALBERT. Submikroskopische Morphologie des Protoplasmas und seiner Derivate. Berlin: Gebr. Borntraeger, 1938.

GARDNER, MARTIN. The Ambidextrous Universe. New York: Basic Books, 1964.

GHYKA, MATILA. The Geometry of Art and Life. New York: Sheed and Ward, 1946.

GILBERT, KATHARINE EVERETT, and HELMUT KUHN. A History of Esthetics. 2nd ed. Indiana University Press, 1953.

GLACKEN, CLARENCE J. Traces on the Rhodian Shore: Nature and Culture in Western Thought from Ancient Times to the End of the Eighteenth Century. University of California Press, 1967.

GODE-VON AESCH, ALEXANDER. Natural Science in German Romanticism. ("Columbia University Germanic Studies," n.s., no. 11.) Columbia University Press, 1941.

GOETHE, JOHANN WOLFGANG VON. Goethe's Botanical Writings. Ed. Bertha Mueller. University of Hawaii Press, 1952.

GOLDSCHMIDT, RICHARD. "Otto Bütschli 1848-1920." *Die Naturwissenschaften*, 8th year (July 9, 1920), pp. 543-49.

————. "Otto Bütschli, Pioneer of Cytology." *In* E. A. Underwood, ed., Science, Medicine and History: Essays . . . in Honour of Charles Singer (1953), pp. 223-232.

————. Portraits from Memory: Recollectitons of a Zoologist. University of Washington Press, 1956.

————. In and Out of the Ivory Tower: The Autobiography of Richard B. Goldschmidt. University of Washington Press, 1960.

GREW, NEHEMIAH. The Anatomy of Plants: With an Idea of a Philosophical History of Plants and Several Other Lectures Read Before the Royal Society [1672-1682]. ("The Sources of Science," no. 11.) New York: Johnson Reprint Corporation, 1965.

GROHMANN, WILL. Paul Klee. New York: Harry N. Abrams, 1955.

GUGGENHEIM, MARGUERITE, ed. Art of This Century . . . with Introductory Essays by André Breton, "Genesis and Perspective of Surrealism"; Hans Arp, "Abstract Art, Concrete Art"; and Piet Mondrian, "Abstract Art." New York: Art Aid Corporation, 1942.

HAECKEL, ERNST. Die Radiolarien (*Rhizopoda Radiolaria*): Eine Monographie. 3 vols. Berlin: Georg Reimer, 1862.

————. Generelle Morphologie der Organismen: Allgemeine Grundzüge der organischen Formen Wissenschaft, mechanisch begründet durch die von Charles Darwin reformirte Descendenz-Theorie. 2 vols. Berlin: Georg Reimer, 1866.

————. "Monograph of Monera." *Quarterly Journal of Microscopical Science,* vol. 9 (1869), pp. 23-44, 113-149, 219-232, and 327-358, and 2 pls.

————. Studien über Moneren und andere Protisten. "Biologische Studien," vol. 1. Leipzig: W. Engelmann, 1870.

————. The History of Creation: Or the Development of the Earth and Its Inhabitants by the Action of Natural Causes.... Trans. E. Ray Lankester. 2 vols. New York: D. Appleton, 1876.

————. Report on the Radiolaria Collected by H.M.S. Challenger During the Years 1873-1876. *In* Sir C. Wyville Thomson and John Murray, Report on the Scientific Results of the Voyage of H.M.S. Challenger During the Years 1873-1876.... Zoology, vol. 18, in 3 pts. London: H. M. Government, 1887.

————. Kunst-Formen der Natur. Leipzig and Vienna: Bibliographischen Instituts, 1899-1904.

————. The Riddle of the Universe at the Close of the Nineteenth Century. Trans. Joseph McCabe. New York: Harper, 1901.

————. The Wonders of Life: A Popular Study of Biological Philosophy. Trans. Joseph McCabe. New York: Harper, 1905.

————. Kristallseelen: Studien über das anorganische Leben. Leipzig: Alfred Kröner, 1917.

————. The Story of the Development of a Youth . . . . Trans. G. Barry Gifford. New York: Harper, 1923.

HAMBRIDGE, JAY. Dynamic Symmetry: The Greek Vase. Yale University Press, 1920.

HAMMOND, WILLIAM A. A Bibliography of Aesthetics and of the Philosophy of the Fine Arts from 1900 to 1932. 2nd ed. New York: Longmans, Green, 1934.

HARRIS, ERROL E. The Foundations of Metaphysics in Science. New York: Humanities Press, 1965.

HENCHMAN, MICHAEL J. "Guts, Positrons and the Origin of Life: Inherent Asymmetry in the Physical World." *Journal of the Leeds University Union Chemical Society,* vol. 5 (1963), pp. 51-60.

HUGHES, ARTHUR. A History of Cytology. London and New York: Abelard-Schuman, 1959.

HUTCHINSON, G. EVELYN. "The Naturalist as Art Critic." *In* The Ecological Theater

and the Evolutionary Play (Yale University Press, 1965), pp. 95-108 and frontisp.

HUXLEY, LEONARD. Life and Letters of Thomas Henry Huxley. 2 vols. New York: D. Appleton, 1901.

HUXLEY, THOMAS HENRY. The Scientific Memoirs of Thomas Henry Huxley. Ed. Michael Foster and E. Ray Lankester. 4 vols. London: Macmillan, 1898-1902.

JAEGER, F. M. Lectures on the Principle of Symmetry and Its Applications in All Natural Sciences. 2nd ed. Amsterdam: Elsevier, 1920.

JANIS, SIDNEY. Abstract and Surrealist Art in America. New York: Reynal & Hitchcock, 1944.

JOHNSON, F. R.—See Boyd, J. D., et al.

JONES, OWEN. The Grammar of Ornament. . . . London: Day and Son [1856].

KANDINSKY, WASSILY. On the Spiritual in Art [1911]. Ed. Hilla Rebay. New York: Solomon R. Guggenheim Foundation, 1946.

KANT, IMMANUEL. Kant's Kritik of Judgment. Trans. J. H. Bernard. London: Macmillan, 1892.

KEPES, GYORGY. Language of Vision. . . . Chicago: Paul Theobald, 1944.

————. The New Landscape in Art and Science. Chicago: Paul Theobald. 1956.

————, ed. The Visual Arts Today. Middletown, Conn.: Wesleyan University Press, 1960.

KLEE, PAUL. The Diaries of Paul Klee 1898-1918. Ed. Felix Klee. University of California Press, 1964.

KOESTLER, ARTHUR. The Act of Creation. New York: Macmillan, 1964.

————. The Ghost in the Machine. New York: Macmillan, 1968.

KOLLER, GOTTFRIED. Das Leben des Biologen Johannes Müller 1801-1858. ("Grosse Naturforscher," vol. 23.) Stuttgart: Wissenschaftliche Verlagsgesellschaft M.B.H., 1958.

KUHN, HELMUT—See Gilbert, K. E.

LANGER, SUZANNE K. Feeling and Form: A Theory of Art Developed from "Philosophy in a New Key." New York: Scribners, 1953.

————. Mind: An Essay on Human Feeling. Vol. 1. Johns Hopkins University Press, 1967.

LECHAVALIER, HUBERT A., and MORRIS, SOLOTOROVSKY. Three Centuries of Microbiology. New York: McGraw-Hill Book Co., 1965.

LEDUC, STÉPHANE ARMAND-NICOLAS. The Mechanism of Life. Trans. W. Deane Butcher. New York: Rebman Co., 1914.

LEIDY, JOSEPH. Fresh-Water Rhizopods of North America. In F. V. Hayden, ed., Report of the United States Geological Survey of the Territories, vol. 12. Washington: U. S. Government Printing Office, 1879.

LEVER, J. D.—See Boyd, J. D., et al.

LEVY, JULIEN. Surrealism. New York: Black Sun Press, 1936.

LEWIS, FREDERICK T. "A Note on Symmetry as a Factor in the Evolution of Plants and Animals." American Naturalist, vol. 57 (1923), pp. 5-41.

————. "The Typical Shape of Polyhedral Cells in Vegetable Parenchyma and the Restoration of That Shape Following Cell Division." Proceedings of the American Academy of Arts and Sciences, vol. 58 (1923), pp. 537-552.

LIDDELL, EDWARD GEORGE TANDY. The Discovery of Reflexes. Oxford: Clarendon Press, 1960.

LOWES, JOHN LIVINGSTON. The Road to Xanadu: A Study in the Ways of the Imagination. Boston and New York: Houghton-Mifflin, 1927.

MACALISTER, ALEXANDER. "On the Law of Symmetry as Exemplified in Animal Forms." Journal of the Royal Dublin Society, vol. 5 (1870), pp. 326-338.

MAGNUS, RUDOLF. Goethe As a Scientist [1906]. Trans. H. Norden. New York: Henry Schuman, 1949.

McKENZIE, GORDON. Organic Unity in Coleridge. ("University of California Publications in English," vol. 7, no. 1.) University of California Press, 1939.

MENDELSOHN, EVERETT. "Physical Models and Physiological Concepts: Explanation in Nineteenth-Century Biology." British Journal for the History of Science, vol. 2 (1965), pp. 201-219.

MILNE-EDWARDS, HENRI. "Mémoire sur la structure élémentaire des principaux tissus organiques des animaux." Archives générales de médicine . . . , 1st year, vol. 3 (September 1823), pp. 165-184.

MOBIUS, KARL. Ästhetik der Tierwelt. Jena: Gustav Fischer, 1908.

NÄGELI, CARL. "Memoir on the Nuclei, Formation, and Growth of Vegetable Cells" [1844]. Trans. Arthur Henfrey. In Henfrey, ed., Reports and Papers on Botany (London: Ray Society, 1846), pp. 213-292 and pl. 7.

————. Entstehung und Begriff der Naturhistorischen Art. 2nd ed. Munich: Königl. Akademie, 1865.

NEEDHAM, JOSEPH. "S. T. Coleridge as a Philosophical Biologist." Science Progress, vol. 20, no. 80 (April, 1926), pp. 692-702.

————. "Organicism in Biology." Journal of Philosophical Studies, vol. 3, no. 9 (January 1928), pp. 29-40.

————. Order and Life. Yale University Press, 1936. [Reprinted in paperback, M.I.T. Press, 1968.]

————. Biochemistry and Morphogenesis. Cambridge University Press, 1942.

NEWTON, ERIC. The Meaning of Beauty. New York: McGraw-Hill, 1950.

NICOLLE, CHARLES. Biologie de l'invention. ("Bibliotheque de philosophie contemporaine.") Paris: Félix Alcan, 1932.

NICOLLE, JACQUES La symétrie dans la nature et les traveaux des hommes. ("Les Conférences du Palais de la Découverte," ser. A, no. 198.) Alençon: Poulet-Malassis, 1954.

NIERENDORF, KARL. Paul Klee: Paintings, Watercolors 1913 to 1939. New York: Oxford University Press, 1941.

NISSEN, CLAUS. "Über Botanikmalerei." Atlantis, vol. 35 (Berlin: 1963), pp. 349-368.

NORDENSKIOLD, ERIK. The History of Biology: A Survey [1920-1924]. Trans. L. B. Eyre. New York: Tudor, 1928.

OKEN, LORENZ. Elements of Physiophilosophy [1809-1811]. Trans. Alfred Tulk. London: Ray Society, 1847.

OZENFANT, AMEDÉE. Foundations of Modern Art. London: John Rodker, 1931.

PASTEUR, LOUIS. "Recherches sur les relations qui peuvent exister entre la forme cristalline, la composition chimique et le sense de la polarisation rotatoire." Annales de chimie et de physique, 3rd ser., vol. 24 (1848), pp. 442-459.

PETTIGREW, J. BELL. Design in Nature: Illustrated by Spiral and Other Arrangements in the Inorganic and Organic Kingdoms As Exemplified in Matter, Force, Life, Growth, Rhythm, etc., Especially in Crystals, Plants, and Animals. . . . 3 vols. London: Longmans, Green, 1908.

PICKEN, L. E. R. "The Fine Structure of Biological Systems." *Biological Reviews of the Cambridge Philosophical Society,* vol. 15 (1940), pp. 133-167.

PITELKA, DOROTHY R. Electron-Microscopic Structure of Protozoa. Oxford: Pergamon Press, 1963.

POLANYI, MICHAEL. Personal Knowledge: Towards a Post-Critical Philosophy [1958]. New York: Harper Torchbooks, 1964.

PORTER, KEITH R., and MARY A. BONNE-VILLE. An Introduction to the Fine Structure of Cells and Tissues. Philadelphia: Lea & Febiger, 1964.

PROCHNOW, OSKAR. Formenkunst der Natur. Berlin: Ernst Wasmuth, [1934].

RAMÓN Y CAJAL, SANTIAGO. "Recollections of My Life." Trans. E. Horne Craigie, assisted by Juan Cano. *Memoirs of the American Philosophical Society,* vol. 8, pts. 1 and 2 (1937).

RHODIN, JOHANNES A. G. An Atlas of Ultrastructure. Philadelphia: W. B. Saunders, 1963.

RIBOT, T. Essai sur l'imagination créatrice. Paris: Félix Alcan, 1900.

RITTERBUSH, PHILIP C. Overtures to Biology: The Speculations of Eighteenth-Century Naturalists. Yale University Press, 1964.

RUBIN, WILLIAM. "Toward a Critical Framework." *Artforum,* vol. 5, no. 1 (September, 1966), pp. 36-55. [Excerpts from Dada and Surrealist Art (New York: Abrams, 1968).]

SCHAEFFER, ASA A. Amoeboid Movement. Princeton University Press, 1920.

SCHENK, ROBERT—See Schmidt, Georg.

SCHLEIDEN, MATTHIAS JACOB. "Contributions to Phytogenesis" [1838]. Trans. Henry Smith. *In* Schwann, Microscopical Researches . . . (1847), pp. 231-268.

————. Principles of Scientific Botany: Or, Botany As an Inductive Science [1842]. Trans. Edwin Lankester. London: Longman, Brown, Green, and Longmans, 1849. [Lacks much of the introduction of the original edition]

————. Poetry of the Vegetable World: A Popular Exposition of the Science of Botany and Its Relations to Man. Trans. Arthur Henfrey. Ed. Alphonso Wood. Cincinnati: Moore, Anderson, Wilstach & Keys, 1853.

SCHMID, GUNTHER. Goethe und die Naturwissenschaften: Eine Bibliographie. Halle: Kaiserlich Leopoldinisch-Carolinisch Deutschen Akademie der Naturforscher, 1940.

SCHMIDT, GEORG, and ROBERT SCHENK. Kunst und Naturform. Basel: Basilius Presse, 1958.

SCHNECKENBERGER, T. CH. Ueber die Symmetrie der Pflanzen: Eine Inaugural-Dissertation . . . . Tübingen: Ludwig Friedrich Fues, 1836.

SCHWABACHER, ETHEL K. Arshile Gorky. Preface by Lloyd Goodrich. Introduction by Meyer Schapiro. New York: Macmillan, 1957.

SCHWANN, THEODORE. Microscopical Researches into the Accordance in the Structure and Growth of Animals and Plants [1838]. Trans. Henry Smith. London: Sydenham Society, 1847.

SEIFRIZ, WILLIAM. "The Alveolar Structure of Protoplasm." *Protoplasma,* vol. 9 (1930), pp. 177-208.

————, ed. A Symposium on the Structure of Protoplasm. Iowa State College Press, 1942.

————. "Protoplasmic Streaming." *Botanical Review,* vol. 9 (1943), pp. 49-123.

SEWELL, ELIZABETH. The Orphic Voice: Poetry and Natural History. Yale University Press, 1960.

SHERRINGTON, SIR CHARLES SCOTT. Goethe on Nature & on Science. Cambridge University Press, 1942.

SINNOTT, EDMUND W. "The Cell and the Problem of Organization." *Science,* vol. 89 (January 20, 1939), pp. 41-46.

————. The Problem of Organic Form. Yale University Press, 1963.

SOLOTOROVSKY, MORRIS—See Lechevalier, H. A.

STRACHE, WOLF. Forms and Patterns in Nature. New York: Pantheon, 1956.

THIMANN, KENNETH V. The Life of Bacteria. 2nd ed. New York: Macmillan, 1963.

STEINBERG, LEO. "The Eye Is a Part of the Mind." *Partisan Review,* vol. 20 (1953), pp. 194-212.

THOMPSON, D'ARCY WENTWORTH. On Growth and Form [1917]. 2nd ed. New York: Macmillan, 1943.

VERNADSKY, W. I. "Problems of Geochemistry, II: The Fundamental Matter-Energy Difference Between the Living and the Inert Natural Bodies of the Biosphere." Trans. George Vernadsky. Abridged by G. Evelyn Hutchinson. *Transactions of the Connecticut Academy of Arts and Sciences,* vol. 35 (1944), pp. 483-517.

WADDINGTON, CONRAD H. Biological Organisation, Cellular and Sub-Cellular: Proceedings of a Symposium Organised on Behalf of UNESCO. London: Pergamon Press, 1959.

————. The Nature of Life. London: Allen & Unwin, 1961.

————. New Patterns in Genetics and Development. New York: Columbia University Press, 1962 (paper, 1966).

WEIDLÉ, WLADIMIR. "Biology of Art: Initial Formulation and Primary Orientation." Trans. E. P. Halperin. *Diogenes,* no. 17 (spring 1957), pp. 1-15.

WEISS, PAUL. "Beauty and the Beast: Life and the Rule of Order." *The Scientific Monthly,* vol. 81 (1955), pp. 286-299.

————. "Organic Form: Scientific and Aesthetic Aspects." *In* Kepes, The Visual Arts Today (1960), pp. 180-194.

————. "1 + 1 ≠ 2 (One Plus One Does Not Equal Two)." *In* Gardner C. Quarton, Theodore Melnechuk, Francis O. Schmitt, The Neurosciences: A Study Program . . . (New York: Rockefeller University Press, 1967), pp. 801-821.

WEYL, HERMANN. Symmetry. Princeton University Press, 1952.

WHYTE, LAWRENCE L., ed. Aspects of Form. University of Indiana Press, 1951. [Paper, 1961.]

WIGGLESWORTH, V. B. The Control of Growth and Form: A Study of the Epidermal Cell in an Insect. Cornell University Press, 1959.

WILSON, EDMUND B. The Cell in Development and Inheritance. New York: Macmillan, 1898.

Index

Abstraction, of the idealized leaf from the plant, 4; in idealistic morphology, 7; all images derived through, 9; gives rise to form, 22; unity of plan in jellyfish, 55; Haeckel's drawings, 64; biological forms in abstract painting, 78-86.

Aberrations, of microscopic images, 46, 56.

Abrams, M., 18.

Accordance, in structure of plants and animals, 31, 31 (fig. 8).

Actinomma drymodes, 65 (fig. 33).

Agalma, 57 (fig. 28).

Alloway, L., 84.

d'Alton, E. J., 5.

Amoeba, spiral path of, 41.

Amoeba proteus, 59 (fig. 29), 90 (fig. 43).

Anderson, E., 91.

Anglim, J., vi.

Anschauung, 2.

Antarctic, 42.

Anthropomorphic view of nature, belief that machines may represent organisms, 33.

Arber, A., 33 (fn. 15).

Arbor Dianae, 14 (fn. 14).

Aristotle, 86, 87.

Arp, H., 78, 85 (fn. 28), 93 (fn. 42).

Art, Goethe as a painter, 5; flower painting, 5, 9; Carus as a painter, 13; likened to organisms, 18, 20; form in, 22; art nouveau, 23; beauty derives from resemblance to nature, 24; the artist's eye in science, 30; mirrored by nature, 40; decorative, ornamental designs, 47; Haeckel as a painter, 64; production of form by organisms compared to, 64; Boveri as a painter, 69-72; art and architecture of viruses, 53 (fn. 13); Leduc's artificial organic forms considered as works of, 76; imitation of the essence of nature, not externals, 78; role of idea of organic form in, distinguished from science, 79; Cajal's ambition to become a painter, 82; negative experimentation in, 83; organic quality of, viewed in terms of structural unity, 86; in natural form, 87; biology of, 87 (fn. 33); *On Growth and Form* as a work of, 88; affinities with science, 82 (fn. 15); organic metaphor for, 85 (fn. 28).

Ascaris, egg in two-celled stage, 70 (fig. 37).

Asymmetry—See "Symmetry."

Bakker, R., 13 (fn. 13).

Baltzer, F., 70 (fn. 41).

Barr, A., 84.

Bary, A. de, 58.

Bathybius Haeckelii, 61 (fig. 31), 66.

Beaumont, J., 14 (fn. 14).

Beauty, in nature, Goethe's sense of, 1-2; more important than scientific understanding, 11; recognition of in Romantic poetry, e.g., *The Ancient Mariner,* 16; sense of in Romantic period contributed to esthetic theory, 23; in Kantian esthetics, 24-25; equated with truth and distinguished from elegance by M. Polanyi, 25 (fn. 23); cell theory exemplifies translation of, into truth, 33-34; symmetry as a quality of, its value in representing reality, adoption in biology, 48; interest of Goodsir and Hay in scientific explanation of, 50; nautilus as the embodiment of, 50; golden section, 51; appreciation in nature by Huxley, 59; sense of wonder advances science, 62; of scientific knowledge, basis of popular understanding of science, 66 (fn. 30); in Leduc's artificial plants, 73; scientific facts transmuted into, 80; silence of reason before, 80; expressiveness of biological forms a reflection of aspirations toward, 85; scientist's sense of, 82 (fn. 15).

Bernal, J. D., 15 (fn. 15).

Berzelius, J. J., 2, 33 (fn. 14).

Bichat, F., 8-9, 46 (fn. 6).

Biology, division into differing schools of thought about form, idealistic morphologists disdaindful of empirical reality and physiologists uninterested in questions of form, 27; the objectification of form leads toward a new synthesis, based upon a rejection of the ideal aspects of form and an acceptance of the scientific value of observations of regularities in the form of organisms, 48.

Biot, J. B., 54.

Blackstone, B., 19.

Blake, W., 17, 19.

Blanshard, F. B., 79 (fn. 11).

Blaue Reiter, 78.

Blood corpuscles, thought to be spherical rather than disc shaped, 28-29.

Blumenbach, J. F., 6 (fn. 5).

Bone, microstructure of, 50.

Bonnet, C., 51.

Bonneville, M. A., 91.

Booth, A., vii.

Bouleau, C., 78.

Boveri, T., 69-72.

Braun, A., 51, 63.

Bravais, A. and L., 51.

Brisseau-Mirbel, C. F., 30.

Brown, R., 30.

Brownian motion, 38.

deBruyn, P. P. H., 68 (fn. 37).

Burke, J. G., 15 (fn. 15).

Bütschli, O., 66-69, 74, 80, 88.

Cajal, R. y, 80-82.

Calandrini, 51.

Candolle, A. P. de, 63 (fn. 27).

Canguilhem, G., 33.

Capillaries, effectiveness is size-limited, 46.

Carlyle, Thomas, 23.

Carritt, E. F., 24 (fn. 21).

Carus, C. G., 12-14.

Cell, complexity of fine structure, 91 (fig. 45).

Cell theory, origins of, 29-32; as an explanation in terms of the organism as a whole, a representation, fulfilling the idea of organic form, 33-34; Owen's denial that protozoa were cells, 43; contribution of Goodsir to, 50; disputed by Huxley, 58.

Cellulose, spiral structure in, 36.

Cézanne, P., 84.

Chain of being, 6.

Chromosomes, symmetry of, 70 (fig. 37).

Chun, C., 69.

Church, A. H., 51.

Clark, M., vii.

Classification, of organisms by Linnaeus, 6; as a representation of reality, 6; based upon circles, 14, 56; based upon symmetry properties of organic forms, 46; of jellyfish by Huxley, 55-56; symmetry as a leading characteristic in, 63.

Cloud, P., 93.

Coccoliths, Huxley's inference from, 60-62.

Cohn, F., 58.

Coleman, W., 9 (fn. 8).

Coleridge, S. T., 16-19, 22, 25; scientific sources for use of organic form in *The Ancient Mariner,* 80, 86.

Cook, J., 80.

Cowan, R. S., vii.

Coxe, D., 14 (fn. 14).

Creativity, plant symbolizing, 12 (fig. 3); imagination as the faculty of, 17; identical in art and science, 18; "theory of vegetable genius," 18-19; organic character of and relation to the unconscious, 23; biological basis of, 19 (fn. 8); nature of, 80; symbolized by organic form, 84-85.

Crick, F., 32 (fn. 13).

Crystallization, growth of organisms identified with, 8, 14; by Schwann, 31-32; by Wulff, 53; by Haeckel, 66; of mineral substances, geometry of, 14-15; spherical (organic) forms distinguished from, 27; presents little anology to organic processes, 32; growth of organisms differs from, Schleiden, 40, and Jaeger, 53; of organic substances, unique symmetry properties, 54; of viruses, 53 (fn. 13); "ich Krystall," P. Klee, 76; organisms known not to be crystalline in structure, 91-92.

Cubists, 84.

Curtis, H., 53 (fn. 13).

Cuvier G., 9, 59.

Cyclops, H.M.S., 60.

Daemonelix, 41 (fn. 26).

Dampier, W., 80.

Darwin, C., 6, 63.

Darwin, E., 19; on spiral vessels of plants, 34, 40.

Davy, H., 2, 17-18.
Denis, M., 82 (fn. 16).
Descartes, R., 48.
Design in nature, history of ideas of, 24 (fn. 21).
Devil's corkscrew, 41 (fn. 26).
DNA, de-oxyribonucleic acid, helical structure of, 91.
Dobell, C., 88.
Doflein, H., 69.
Don, D., 36 (fn. 21).
Driesch, H., 71.
Duchamp, M., 82, 84 (fn. 26).
Dujardin, F., 43-46.
Dutrochet, H., 28.

Ehrenberg, C. G., 42-43, 60.
Eliot, T. S., 86.
Enantiomorphs, 54.
Environmental influence on organisms, size of plans, 3; should be expressed in art, 5; molecular-level phenomena determined by, 58.
Epithelial layers or foundation membranes in jellyfish, 56 (fig. 27).
Ernst, M., 83, 85.
Esenbeck, N. von, 13.
Esthetics, exalted over science by Goethe, 11; analysis of the experience of beauty, 16; belief that images of nature are fitted to the mind, 19; definition of organic form, 20-21; source of guiding principles in science, 22; treats of form abstracted from works of art, 22; Kantian, 24-25; corollaries of idea of organic form, 25; influences interpretation of microscopic images, 30; reductionist belief that forms of organisms are reducible to laws of physics and chemistry as an esthetic principle, 32; establishment of cell theory exemplifies constructive consequences of the guiding influence of esthetics on scientific research, 34; greater symmetry at the microscopic level, 46; harmony, proportion, rhythm, 47-48; sensibilities of Goodsir, strength of, 50; presupposition of unity of plan in siphonophores, 55; functionalism, affinity between Huxley and Kant, 59; Romantic, ideal form, influence on Huxley, despite his disavowal of idealistic morphology, 62; sense of wonder promotes science, 62; presuppositions of, led Haeckel to misinterpret observations of radiolaria, 64; presuppositions of, led Bütschli to a false interpretation of microscopic observations, 68; underlay use of organic form in twentieth-century art, 79; satisfaction of esthetic instincts in science, Cajal, 82; Aristotelian concept of structural unity distinguished from organic form, 86; Langer, 87; contributions to science, 82 (fn. 15).
Evolution, theory of, 3, 6, 63.

Explanation, scientific, of organisms, lacking in 1800, 2; through representations referring to categories of, 7, 9-10; mechanical, for growth and form, 8; less interesting to Goethe than esthetic satisfaction, 11; concepts drawn from restricted phenomena will not be satisfactory explanations of less restricted phenomena, Wigner, 32; mechanisms are illustrations only, not representations of organisms, 33; biology seeks a representation of the organism as a whole, 33; of microscopic events required recognition of new principles, 46; Huxley's view of, 58. See also "Science."

Fawcett, D. W., 89 (fn. 38).
Fechner, G. T., 23.
Fibonacci series, 51, 52 (fig. 23).
Flustra gayi, 47 (fig. 20).
Foam structure of protoplasm, diagram of, 67 (fig. 34).
Foraminifera, 43.
Forbes, E., 56 (fn. 17).
Form, essential, quoting Goethe, 3; treatment in poems of Keats and Darwin, 19-20; seen as a result of growth, 20; defined in biology, 20, in art, 22; universality of perception of, in Kantian esthetics, 24; means whereby visual faculty contributes to understanding [See "Kant"], 5; geometry and the molecular theory of crystal growth, 15; pattern of cells, 31; independence of size of organism, in idealistic morphology, 43; dependence upon size of organism recognized by Dujardin, 45-46; of protozoa typical of minute living system, 45-46; symmetry principles found applicable to, 46; of logarithmic spiral, 48; mechanical basis of laws of growth indicated by regularities in, 48-50; Newtonian laws of, 50; traced to molecular-level phenomena, 54; esthetic presuppositions influence preception of, by Haeckel, by Bütschli, 68; generation by organism seen as work of art, 64; perception of, facilitated by esthetic sense of scientists, 69; importance of, in genetic material, 70; osmotic growths resulting from rhythm of altered concentration in solutions, 74; transmutation of, in creative act, 79-80; biomorphic, 84; inseparable from function in molecular architecture of living systems, 91-92. See also "Spiral," "Structure."
Form, ideal, 5, 8; central object of Romantic morphology, 11; Herder's concept of, 11; Oken on, 11; in *Naturphilosophie,* 11; sphere as, 11; circles in McLeay's conjectural scheme of classification, 13-14, 56; Greek vases, in E. Darwin and Keats, 19-20; symmetry properties of, 20 (fn. 12); similarity or congruity of whole and parts in idealistic morphology, 26-29; the sphere, 27; belief that blood corpuscles were spherical, 28-29; spiral, 34-

41; polygastric theory of protozoa as instance of belief in unity of plan in all organisms, 17-19; became objectified, 48; unity of plan, esthetic presuppposition of Huxley, 55-63; Huxley's opposition to cell theory because it failed to satisfy his idea of, 58; Huxley's strictures upon, 60; ruled out by Thompson, 89.

Form, interpretation of, latitude afforded by early microscopes, 29, 39; polygastric (many stomachs) theory of protozoan structure, 42-46, 60; higher degrees of symmetry among microscopic forms, 46; basic structure of jellyfish understood by Huxley, 55; coccoliths seen as evidence for *Urschleim*, 60-61; Haeckel misled by esthetic presuppositions, 64; fine structure of protoplasm, Bütschli misled by esthetic presuppositions, 68-69; role of esthetics in, 80-81.

Form, objectification of, central development in history of morphology, 25; resolves dichotomy between idealistic morphology and reductionist physiology, 34 [See also "Biology"]; exemplified in study of spiral structure, 36; in microscopy, 39; paradigm of the history of morphology, 34; fostered by Dujardin's recognition of the role of size in determining structure, 45-46; repetitive structure arises from rhythms in growth, 47; symmetry principles in, 47; from ideal form to mathematical regularity, nautilus as an example of, 48; establishment of symmetry properties unique to organisms as the objectification of the idea of organic form, 53; asymmetry of organic processes, demonstration by Pasteur, 55; synapses, 81; climaxed in Thompson, *On Growth and Form,* 87-88; in DNA, 91.

Form, organic, aspects of. In Goethe's morphology, as relation of part to whole, 67; Oken and the sphere, 11; distinction between organic and crystalline form, 14; five-fold symmetry unique to organisms, 15; symmetry of higher organisms distinguished from that of crystals, 15 (fn. 15); Coleridge's contribution to ideas of, 16-19; principal statement of, by Coleridge, 20; correspondence in Romantic theory of imagination, 18; attributes of idea in Coleridge's theory, 20-21; in Wordsworth's *The Prelude,* 22-23; sign of spontaneity rather than deliberation, 23; art nouveau, 23; influence upon course of biological discovery in the nineteenth century, 25; distinguished from continuity principle in the scale of beings, 25; distinguished from Aristotelian concept of the unity of structure, 25; guiding esthetic principle in the development of the cell theory, 29-32; influence upon interpretations of microscopic images, 30; cannot be explained

by mechanical processes, 32; meets need for new principle of understanding required by microscopic-level phenomena in organisms, 46; symmetry principles as criteria of, 47-48; logarithmic spiral, 48-53, Goodsir's fascination by, 50; golden section, 51; spiral arrangements distinguished from crystal lattice, 53; five-fold radial symmetry in, 54; asymmetry of organic processes, 54; confirmation of uniqueness of, through disproof of spontaneous generation, 55; Huxley's view that mechanical processes determine chemical change but not overall achieved form, 58; shape of coccoliths leads Huxley to suppose they were generated by primordial life substance, 61; use of criteria of, in judging unknown objects, 62; morphology as the science of, 63; denial of uniqueness by Haeckel led to erroneous interpretation of radiolarian structure, 66; denial of uniqueness by Bütschli led to erroneous interpretation of protoplasmic fine structure, 69; Boveri's intuition of, 72; artificially created by Leduc, 73-76; artificially created by G. Kepes, 74-75; emergent order at microscopic level, 76; Klee's delight in, 76-77; in Kandinsky, 79; roles in science and art distinguished, 79; in the unconscious, 80; golden section in Mondrian, 82-83; and Surrealism, 83-85; distinguished from Aristotelian concept of structural unity, 86; formal criteria derived from, governing selection of works of art in the exhibit, 86; in Gestalt psychology and Langer's theory of mind, 87; in Thompson, 88-89; value in investigating ultrastructure, 92; E. Sinnott, 92; J. Needham, 92; C. Waddington, 92-93; P. Weiss, 93; formal criteria used in interpreting the character of micro-fossils or "organized entitles," in meteorites, 93. See also "Spiral," "Structure."

Frey-Wyssling, A., 89 (fn. 38).

Fritsch, F. E., 61.

Galvani L., 2.

Galvanism, as the life force, 26.

Gardner, M., 55 (fn. 14).

Gauguin, P., 84.

Ghyka, M., 82-83.

Gittleman, L., 75 (fn. 5).

Glacken, C., 24 (fn. 21).

Globular theory of tissue, 27-29.

Goethe, J. W. von, scientific interests, 3-5; intuition and insight, 2, 3; visual character of, 5, 7; esthetic ideas, 1, 5; speculative approach, 2-3; tour of Italy, 3-4; primal plant, 4-5; "Metamorphosis of Plants," 4, 7; theory of the vertebrate skull, 4; *Farbenlehre,* 5; morphology, 7, idealistic character of, 7, characterized as illustrating but not representing nature, 9; sacrifice of science to esthetic ideals, 11; and *Naturphilosophie,* 11; defense of St. Hilaire's idealistic morphology, 13; likened artistic career to the life of a plant, 18, 20; *Wilhelm Meister* as the perfect organic work of art, 21; limitations upon his adherence to the idea of organic form, 25; considered whole to be similar to or congruent with the parts, 26, 35; spiral growth of plants, fascination with, 34-35, 40-41; interest of Goodsir in, 50; interest of Huxley in, 62; credited by Haeckel as co-founder of evolutionary theory, 63.

Golden section, 51, 82-83, 88-89.

Goldschmidt, R., 69.

Grandville, pseudonym of Paul-Isidore Gerard, 83.

Granit, R., 82 (fn. 15).

Grew, N., 8, 14, 34.

Gromia fluviatilis, 45 (fig. 19).

Haeberlin, C., 13 (fn. 13).

Haeckel, E. H., 63-66; gastraea theory, 56; work on radiolaria, 63; symmetry properties as the basis for classification, 63; distortion in representations, 64; denial of uniqueness of organic form by, 64; representations of organisms considered as works of art, 64; *Kunst-Formen der Natur,* illustration from, 47 (fig. 20), 66; belief in primordial organic substance, 66, 69, 88.

Haist, G., 75 (fn. 5).

Hales, S., 2.

Hamilton, D., vii.

Hardy, W. H., 92.

Harris, E., 33 (fn. 14).

Harrison, R. G., 79, 82 (fn. 15).

Hartmann, K. R. E. von, 23.

Harvey, W., vi.

Haüy, R. J., 15.

Hegel, G. W. F., 11.

Herder, J. G., 4, 11.

Hermann, L., vii.

Herrick, C. H., 41 (fn. 25).

Hertwig, O., 69.

Home, E., 27-28.

Homeomeriae, 35.

Hooke, R., 14 (fn. 14).

Hooker, J., 42.

Howe, C., vii.

Hulme, T. E., 86.

Humboldt, A. von, 6 (fn. 5); 38 (fn. 23); 42.

Hunter, J., 2.

Hutchinson, G. E., vi.

Huxley, T. H., 55-63; esthetic presuppositions and the discovery of the principles of classification of coelenterates, 55-56; idea of organic form, statement by, 58; positivism, 58; opposition to cell theory, 58; protoplasm, 58; Kantian view of function in esthetic judgments, 59; sense of beauty in nature, 59, 62; stated opposition to idealistic morphology, 60; studies of radiolaria, 60; "Bathybius," 61; sense of wonder, 62; translation of Goethe by, 62.

Hydrozoa, 56.

Hyman, L. H., 63 (fn. 28).

Illustrations, distinguished from representations, 9; machines as illustrations only, not representations, of organisms, 33; of parts, of less explanatory value than representations of the whole, 33; scientific, Goethe's interest in, 5; example of by Goethe, 7 (fig. 3), 9; example of by Carus, 12 (fig. 3); must be executed by the scientific observer, 38; examples of Huxley's, 56; grafting experiment drawn by Klee, 77 (fig. 41); exaggerations of esthetic regularities in Haeckel's, 64; what had not been drawn had not been seen, 70; superiority of Boveri's to Driesch's, 71; Leduc's osmotic growths considered as, 74.

Images, role in idealistic morphology, 7; abstracted from nature, 9; Goethe's, of ideal plant, 10; microscopic, interpretation influenced by esthetic presuppositions, 30; value in analyzing scientific thought and the history of science, 33.

Imagination, faculty required for an understanding of the whole and thus of life, 16-17; distinguished from association of ideas, 17; creative aspects recognized by Davy, 18; excesses of *Naturphilosophie* attributed to, by Schleiden, 38; influence of microorganisms upon, 42; led Haeckel and Bütschli to report the existence of illusory structures, 63-69; Lowes' account of, in Coleridge, 80.

Infusoria—See "Protozoa."

Ingenhousz, J., 2.

Insects, plants analogous to, 36.

Jaeger, F. M., 53 (fig. 25), 55.

James, H., 86.

Kandinsky, W., 78, 84.

Kant, I., 21-22, 24-25, 49, 59.

Kauffmann, A., 5.

Keats, J., 19-20, 78.

Kepes, G., 74-75.

Kepler, J., 51.

Kessel, J. van, 9.

Klee, P., 76-79; "ich Krystall," 76; crystal lattice and organic space frame, 76-78; "expressive" forms at Naples aquarium, 76; studies of anatomy, 77; collections of natural objects, 77; "spatial organism," 77.

Kölliker, R., 63.

Koelreuter, J., 3.

Kuhn, T., 34 (fn. 18).

Kupferman, L., 84.

Langer, S., 47 (fn. 7), 87.

Lavoisier, A., 2.
Leaf insertions, sequence of, 51.
Leduc, S. A.-N., 73-74, 88.
Leeuwenhoek, A. von, 28.
Leidy, J., 59.
Leonardo da Vinci, 51.
Lerner, A., vii.
Leslie, J., 48.
Lhote, A., 82.
Liddell, E. G. T., 81 (fn. 14).
Liebig, J. von, 33 (fn. 14).
Liesebang, R., 74.
Life, Coleridge's definition of, 16; hierarchical levels of organization in, 32; universally diffused, 42; essence of, expressed by golden section, 51; essential asymmetry of, 54.
Link, H. F., 38.
Linnaeus, C., 6, 7, 19 (fn. 10).
Lister, J. J., and Hodgkin, 30 (fn. 10).
Logarithmic spiral, 49 (fig. 22), 88-89.
Lorenz, K., 82 (fn. 15).
Lovejoy, A. O., 6.
Lowe, H., vii.
Lowes, J. L., 80.
Lomax, Lucius E., vii.
Lundquist, C., vii.

Mach, E., 47 (fn. 7).
MacLuhan, M., 33.
Magnus, R., 4 (fn. 3).
Marc, F., 78.
Marquardt, J., vii.
Mason, R., vii.
Masson, A., 83, 85.
Mast, S. O., 89.
Matisse, H., 84.
Matta, frontisp., 84.
Maupertuis, P., 14.
Mayer, A. G., 57.
McKenzie, G., 17 (fn. 2).
McLeay, W. S., 13-14, 56.
Mechanical processes, sufficient to explain crystal structure, 14; geometrical form indicates operation of, 15; insufficient to account for phenomena of life, 16, 32; distinguished from indwelling creative energies, 18; geometrical quality in forms an indication of, 48; force a function of the mass of an organism, 48-50; inadequacy of, to produce life, shown by Pasteur, 55; determine chemical changes of proteins, but not the achieved forms of organisms, 58; responsible for the forms of organisms, within a "field of force," according to Thompson, 88.
Mechanist-vitalist controversy, 32.
Meckel, J. F., 28.
Medusae, jellyfish, 55.
Mendelsohn, E., 32-33.
Metabolic phenomena, 32.
Metamorphosis of plants, 36-38.

Meyen, J., 45 (fn. 5).
Microscope, 5, 9, 27-30, 36, 39, 43, 89.
Millais, J. E., 23.
Milne-Edwards, H., 28.
Miró, J., 83.
Models, scientific constructs for reality, 6; role in scientific explanation, 6; classification as, 6; for organic fine structure in seventeenth century, 8; as representations of reality, 10; crystals as, of plants, 14; historian seeks to provide an account of the scientific significance of, and intellectual presuppositions relating to, 33; function as illustrations of one kind of phenomenon in terms of another, 33; foam, for protoplasm, 67.
Moholy-Nagy, L., 74.
Molluscan shell, spirals of, 48-51.
Mondrian, P., 82-83, 84.
Monera, 66.
Moore, H., 93 (fn. 42).
Morphology, ideal type in, 5; Goethe, 7; analytic, exemplified by N. Grew, 8; further exemplified by Dutrochet's belief that organisms were aggregates of globules, 29; further exemplified by Schleiden's view of spiral structures, 36; statement of the idea of organic form, 25; cell theory as foundation of, 31; objectification of ideal forms in, 48; objectification of the idea of organic form, 53; Huxley's strictures upon idealistic morphology, 60; Haeckel's treatise on, 63; symmetry concepts in, 63; Leduc's artificial growths, 74; Thompson's *On Growth and Form*, 87-88.
Moseley, H., 48.
Müller, J., 5, 63.

Nature, Goethe's idea of, 1; portrait of, 5; orphic concept of, 10; likened to the artist producing forms, 20; beauty of, in Kantian esthetics, 24-25; mirroring art, 40; essence of, revealed by poetry, 38 (fn. 23); essence imitated in art, 78-79; imitation in art, 86.
Nature, 62.
Naturphilosophie, 11-14, 15, 25, 27, 30, 38, 40, 46, 47, 63, 66.
Nautilus, 49 (fig. 21), 83.
Needham, J., 14 (fn. 14), 92.
Neuron theory, 80.
Newton, I., 5, 17.
Newtonianism in science, 2.
Nietzsche, F. W., 23.
Nucleus, of cells, 30.

Oil drop, representation of amoeba, 67 (fig. 35).
Oken, L., 11, 14; monad theory of organic structure, 26-27, 40, 62.
Organic nature, portrait of, by Wilbrand and Ritgen, 6; tree as, 6; beauty in, perceived by Romantic poets, 16; galvanism as the

basis of, 26; unity of plan in, 31, 43; multitudes of unseen organisms, 42; compared to a poem, by Huxley, 59-60.
Osmotic vegetation, 75 (fig. 40).
Owen, R., 43, 48, 60.

Pallas, P. S., 6.
Pantin, C. F. R., 82 (fn. 15).
Paradigm, 34.
Pasteur, L., 51 (fn. 14), 54.
Pearson, K., 82 (fn. 15).
Peterson, A. O., 41 (fn. 26).
Phyllotaxis, 51-54.
Physalia, 55.
Pineapple, arrangement of fruits in, 53 (fig. 25).
Pitelka, D. R., 91.
Plenitude of living beings, 42.
Polygastric theory, criticized by Huxley, 60.
Plants, ideal form of, 3; Urpflanze, 3; primal, 4-5; metamorphosis of, 5; distinguished from animals, 6; as metaphor for kingdoms of organic nature, 6; symbolizing man's mental life, 13; grown like crystals from solutions, 14; symbolizing man's imagination, 18; theory of vegetable genius in Young, Schlegel, Goethe, and Coleridge, 18-19; sensitive, 28; cellular structure of, 30; spiral growth of, 34-40; analogous to insects, 36; spiral leaf arrangements and their symmetry properties, 51-53; artificial, 74; Klee's fascination for, 77.
Poetry, Goethe's Urworte poems, 10; Sherrington, a scientist who wrote, 10; similar concepts in, of Keats and Darwin, 19-20; Schleiden deplores intermingling of, with science in Naturphilosophie, 38; spirit of, discloses truth about nature, 38 (fn. 23); poesy intermingled with esthetic feelings in Goodsir, 50; Huxley's view that nature is more like a poem than a machine, 59-60; Bütschli's gift for, 69.
Poetry, quotations of, from Goethe, "Metamorphosis of the Plants," 4; from Coleridge, The Ancient Mariner, 16; from Davy, "The Sons of Genius," 17; from Darwin, The Botanic Garden, 19, 36; from Keats, Sleep and Poetry, 19, "I Stood Tip-Toe," 20; from Wordsworth, The Prelude, 22-23; from Whitman, Leaves of Grass, 42; from Holmes, "The Pearly Nautilus," 50-51.
Polanyi, M., 15 (fn. 15), 25 (fn. 23), 33 (fn. 16), 66 (fn. 30), 82 (fn. 15).
Policard, A., 90.
Porter, K. R., 91.
Positivism, 58.
Priestley, J., 2, 80.
Prochnow, O., 75.
Protoplasm, "sarcode," 43; pseudopods in foraminifera, 43; establishment of a proper understanding of, 58; "physical basis of life," 58; complexity of, in 1869, 59 (fig. 29), in

1925, 90 (fig. 43), and in 1944, 90 (fig. 44); Huxley's "Bathybius," 61; attribution of a soul to, 64; "monera" as forms of, 66; foam structure of, 67-69; illustration of network structure in, 69.
Protozoa, 5, polygastric (many stomachs) theory of structure, 42-46; widely diffused through the world, 42; "Milky Way" of organisms, 42; cellular character of, denied by Owen, 43; composed of "sarcode," 43; foraminifera, 43; symmetry of, 46, 58.
Purkinje, J., 5.

Radiata, 55.
Radiolaria, discovery by Huxley, 60; monograph by Haeckel, 63; illustrations by Haeckel, 64-65.
Rattlesnake, H.M.S., cruise of, 55.
Ray, M., 74.
Réaumur, R.A.F. de, 2.
Redon, O., 76.
Representations of reality, defined, 9-10; biological classifications as, 6; Cuvier's scientific illustrations as, 9; distinguished from "illustrations," 9; Grew's model for plant structure as, 9; role of symmetry in, 47-48; distorted by esthetic presuppositions of Haeckel, 64, and Bütschli, 68-69; works of art as, 87.
Rhythm, 47.
Richards, I. A., 17 (fn. 1), 86.
Ripley, S. D., iv.
Ritgen, F. A. von, 6 (fn. 5).
Ritterbush, P. C., 2 (fn. 1), 19 (fn. 9), 26 (fn. 1), 38 (fn. 23).
Romantic movement, rejection of empiricism in science, 3; ideal form and Romantic nature philosophy, 11; synthesis in esthetic theory, 21; beauty in nature, 23; delight in idealistic morphology, 48; influence of, seen through persistence of esthetic ideals associated with ideal form, 62; role of organic form in, likened to role of organic form in Surrealism, 84-85.
Romé de l'Isle, J. B., 15.
Ross, J. C., 42.
Rotation of polarized light by asymmetric isomers, 54.
Rubin, W., 84-85.
Ruskin, J., 23.

Sachs, J. von, 69, 70.
St. Hilaire, G., 13.
Sarcode, 43.
Saussure, N. T. de, 2.
Schaeffer, A., 41.
Schelling, F. W. J., 11, 22, 25.
Schiffrin, André, iii.
Schimper, F. K., 51.
Schlegel, A. W. von, 18, 21, 25.

Schleiden, M. J., cell theory, 30-31; spiral forms, 34-40.
Schultze, M., 58.
Schuster, J., 6 (fn. 5).
Schwann, T., 30, 31-32.
Scyphozoan jellyfish, 55-57, 57 (fig. 28).
Science, empiricism in, metaphor of untying a knot, 2; careful observers of organisms, 2; limited explanation in, 3; not less visual than poetry, 10; sacrificed to esthetic ideals by Goethe, 11; affinities with art exemplified by Carus, 13; advancement of, through objectification of form, e.g., cell theory, 29-32, 34; empiricism exemplified in Schleiden, 30; employment of visual images in, 33; should be free of poetry, Schleiden argues, 38; establishment of cell theory exemplifies constructive contribution of esthetic presuppositions in, 34; relation to beauty, 50; positivism in, statement by Huxley, 58; advancement of, through sense of wonder, 62; effect of esthetics upon, demonstrated by divergence of Haeckel's drawings from reality, 63-64; also of Bütschli's idea of foam structure in protoplasm, 69; importance of visual sense in, 69; importance of esthetic sensibilities to the scientist, 70, 82 (fn. 15); role of the idea of organic form in, distinguished from role of that idea in art, 79.
Sculpture, projective, 75.
Seifriz, W., 41, 89 (fn. 38).
Senebier, J., 2.
Sérusier, P., 82.
Sewell, E., 10 (fn. 10).
Shakespeare, W., 21, 69.
Shelley, P. B., 17.
Sherrington, C. S., 4 (fn. 3), 10.
Shropshire, W., vii.
Sinnott, E., 92.
Siphonophores, 55.
Skull, theory of vertebrate, Goethe, 4, 10; Oken, 11; Carus, 13; history of, 13 (fn. 12); Owen, 43; critique by Huxley, 60.
Southey, R., 18.
Species, recognition of, 9, role of esthetics in, 82 (fn. 15).
Speculation, Goethe's, 2, 11; in *Naturphilosophie*, 87-89; esthetic character exemplified by Carus, 13; promoted by ideal form, as exemplified by McLeay, 13-14, or the spiral, 40-41.
Spiral, Oken, 11-13; Wordsworth, 22; E. Darwin, 34; Goethe, 34-35, 35 (fig. 9); transcends mechanical forces, 35; *Vallisneria*, 35, 37 (fig. 10); generated by female forces, 36; of cell walls, 36, 37 (fig. 11); tree trunks, 41; blindfolded man's path exemplifying "the spiral urge," 41; supposed by Dujardin to lack symmetry, 46; molluscan shell, 48-51; Goodsir's fascination with, 50;

"genetic spiral," 53 (fig. 25); Max Ernst, 83.
Spontaneous generation, 55.
Staining, early use of by Schleiden, 36.
Stein, E. von, 3.
Steinberg, L., 85.
Stereochemistry, 55.
Stoba, L., 79 (fn. 11).
Stomach animals, 43.
Structure, unity of, in a work of art, distinguished from organic form, 86.
Structure of organisms, ignored by Goethe and idealistic morphologists, 7; globular theory of tissues, 26-30; cell theory, 29-32; spiral construction of cell walls, 36; spiral tendency traced to structure of protoplasm, 41; polygastric theory of protozoan structure, 42-46; considered to be independent of size of organism by idealistic morphologists, 43; recognized as dependent upon size by Dujardin, 45-46; rhythms of growth, influence upon, 47; symmetry properties of, in phyllotaxis, 51-54; in siphonophores, elucidated by Huxley, 55; Bütschli's studies of protoplasm, 66-69; of chromosomes, esthetic basis of Boveri's recognition of continuity in, 70-71; of nerves, 81; of DNA, 91. See also "Spiral," "Skull, theory of vertebrate," "Crystallization."
Sydow, E. von, 13 (fn. 13).
Symmetry, plant stem as axis of, 4, 51; in crystal structure, 15; shell of "more worth" than Euclid's *Elements,* 22; foretaste of knowledge, 24; in Greek vases, 20 (fn. 12); perfection of, in higher animals, 46; definition of, 46; bilateral, 47 (fig. 20); relations to rhythm, 47; logarithmic spiral, 48; role in esthetics studied by Goodsir and Hay, 50-51; phyllotaxis, concepts relating to, 51-54; distinctiveness of, in organisms, 53-54; asymmetry in organic processes, 54; of scyphozoans, 55; demonstrated in siphonophores, 55; properties of a radiolarian, 65 (fig. 32); search for fine structure of protoplasm, 69; recognition in arrangement of chromosomes led Boverei to assert importance of chemical structure in heredity, 70; of form equated with that of forces in the organism by Thompson, 88; in DNA, 91. See also "Form," "Spiral."

Tanguy, Y., 84.
Tartaric acid, crystals of, 54 (fig. 26).
Taylor, F. A., vi.
Tchelichew, P., 84.
Thalassicola, 61 (fig. 30).
Thompson, D'A. W., 51 (fn. 12), 64, 87-89.
Thomson, W., 62.
Tissue culture, 79.
Towe, K., vii.
Trachelius ovum, 44 (fig. 16).

Tree, metaphor for kingdoms of nature, 6.
Trembley, A., 2.
Twitty, V. C., 82 (fn. 15).

Vallisneria, 37 (fig. 10).
Vélins du Muséum Nationale d'Histoire Naturelle, 66.
Vernadsky, W. I., **55 (fn. 14).**
Vicq d'Azyr, F., 14.
Villon, J., 82.
Unconscious, organic symbol for its role in human sensibility, 12 (fig. 3); unifies man and nature, 22; stratum from which organic forms arise, 23; organic form arises from, 80.
Understanding, Goethe's appetite for, 3; visual basis of, for Goethe, 5; through knowledge of the whole rather than the parts, 8-9; visual basis in Romantic esthetic theory, 19; the "unknown tongue, which yet I understood" as a metaphor for the power of organic forms to suggest significant truth, 22; fitted to nature in Kantian esthetics, 24; of microscopic realm could not be transferred from macroscopic, 46; popular, of science, aided by beauty, 66 (fn. 30).
Urpflanze, 3.
Urschleim, 61.

Virchow, R., 50.
Volta, A., 2.
Vorticella, 44 (fig. 17).

Waddington, C. H., 92-93.
Walkey, F. P., 75 (fn. 5).
Wallich, G. C., 61.
Wardlaw, C. M., 89 (fn. 37).

Watson, J., 91.
Weidlé, W., 87 (fn. 33).
Weiss, P., 93.
Wenzel, C. and J., 27.
Weyl, H., 47 (fn. 7), 51 (fn. 12).
Whitehead, A. N., 19.
Whole, distinguished from parts, as the object of scientific understanding, 8-9; phenomena of life seen as properties of, 16-17; greater than the sum of its parts, 20-21; according to idealistic morphology, thought to be similar to each of the parts or congruent with them, 26-28, 35; reductionism merely illustrates the parts of an organism, leaving unfulfilled the aim of scientific explanation in biology, which is to represent the whole, 33-34; Driesch's belief that the whole organism could be regenerated by any part, 71; intuition of, Boveri's comment on, 72; each part as an embodiment of, Klee, 78; primacy of, 88.
Wigner, E., 32.
Wilbrand, J. B., 6 (fn. 5).
Wilde, O., 40.
Wilenski, R. H., 84 (fn. 25).
Wilson, E. B., 70.
Wimsatt, W. K., quoted, 24.
Wöhler, F., 33 (fn. 14).
Wolff, C. F., 7.
Wordsworth, W., 16, 17; dream from *The Prelude* exemplifying idea of organic form, 22-23.
Wulff, G. W., 53.

Young, E., 18.

Zaunick, R., 13 (fn. 12).